Physical Anthropology
and the Origin of Man

Human Evolution

Gabriel W. Lasker

Wayne State University

Adapted by Frank N. Paparello, Director of Science Services,
Holt, Rinehart and Winston, from *The Evolution of Man*.

 Holt, Rinehart and Winston, Inc., New York

Gabriel W. Lasker, Associate Professor, Wayne State University, has done anthropological field work in China, Mexico, and Peru and has published numerous studies on the physical anthropology of the peoples of these places. He is an editor of "The Teaching of Anthropology" (University of California Press, 1963) and is President of the American Association of Physical Anthropologists.

Preface

This book is an adaptation of a college textbook (*The Evolution of Man, a brief introduction to physical anthropology*) and is addressed primarily to high-school students engaged in the study of biological or social science. The assumption has been made that none of the problems of human evolution, not even the question of the origin of life, are too difficult or too technical to include, provided that a full explanation is made. Unsolved problems are presented as such. Diverse opinions are sometimes presented, but the author has indicated those which he considers most probable.

There are relatively meager resources for teaching about human evolution to high-school students. No suitable film strips or movies are available, although the American Institute of Biological Sciences is in the process of preparing a movie on the subject. There are a number of good movies of non-human primates in the wild, the best of which is one called "Baboon Behavior" filmed by Irven De Vore and S. L. Washburn and available from the Audiovisual Division, Extension Service, University of California, Berkeley, California. Series of 2″ × 2″ colored slides of fossils pertinent to the study of human evolution are available from the audiovisual center at the University of Wisconsin, Madison, Wisconsin. Casts of fossil human remains are available from the University of Pennsylvania Museum in Philadelphia. Few high schools own slide collections and museum materials, as yet, and the chief resource for teaching about human evolution is in the anthropology departments of our great natural history museums. The author hopes that many of the readers will have an opportunity to visit such a museum—where they can see fossils and casts, reconstructions, and displays explaining some of the matters to be dealt with in this book.

In the following pages the first matters to be considered are the nature and origin of life and the essential role of genetic transmission and modification (which is evolution). Man's relationship to other animals is then explored. Then follows a section on fossil remains of man's ancestors and of other fossil primates. These chapters have been completely rewritten to present a simple and logical scheme. The probable succession of developments is presented without labeling each discovery with a separate name. A classification of the fossils is used which is based on criteria gained from the study of the genetics of living men. By these standards there can have been only a few species of man and rarely, if ever, more than one at a time. In this book many of the fossil "species" are therefore eliminated as distinct entities. Though other views are still held by some competent physical anthropologists, and these questions deserve further study with an open mind, an increasing number of scholars of the subject favor views similar to those expressed here. Finally, there is a chapter dealing with measurement of man and the applications of these techniques to the study of growth and other matters affecting human welfare.

In addition to those who aided the author during the preparation of the college text, he is deeply grateful to the authors of critical reviews (including E. W. Count, D. F. Roberts, A. J. Kelso, and E. E. Hunt, Jr.). The author's colleagues Morris Goodman and Harry Maisel made several helpful suggestions and the author's father, Bruno Lasker, again reviewed the whole manuscript and made numerous suggestions for revision large and small. Although not all the criticisms have been heeded, the author is grateful to those who have offered them.

Gabriel W. Lasker
Detroit
March, 1963

Contents

Page

1 Physical Anthropology as a
  Field of Science   7

2 Evolution   11

3 The Biological Basis of Life   19

4 Population Genetics   33

5 Man in the Animal Kindom   43

6 The Order Primates   47

7 Evolutionary Processes and
  Paleontological Principles   61

8 Some Fossil Primates   69

9 Fossil Man   79

10 Measurement of Man   95

11 Evolution and the Future   103

   Bibliography   109

   Glossary   111

   Index   115

1

Physical Anthropology as a Field of Science

"Anthropology," from the Greek *anthropos*, man, and *logos*, knowledge, means the study of man. *Physical anthropology* is the study of man's evolution and biological variation. It tries to explain the source and direction of variation both in individuals and groups, past and present. Thus, it includes the study of fossil man. Many ancient bones similar to those of man are now known; and their meaning for the study of man will be considered later. Much of the progress made in this direction is the work of archeologists and paleontologists. *Archeologists*, students of ancient man and his works, have excavated and studied both bones and tools of prehistoric man. *Paleontologists* have searched for and, when found, examined and reconstructed skeletons of animals—of types now extinct—that may have been the forerunners of man. To the paleontologists we also owe our knowledge of the fishes, horses, dinosaurs, and other animals and plants of past ages, hence also of natural evolution in general. Paleontologists, along with historical geologists, have also provided reliable dates for a study of the tempo and duration of human evolution.

Physical anthropology relies heavily upon studies of the anatomy of present-day vertebrates (animals with backbones) and especially of the group to which man belongs, the *primates*. It relates the study of the anatomy of these present-day animals to the information gained from fossil studies. The study of man and his place in nature involves not only the physical anthropologist and the anatomist, but also those biologists whose special areas of investigation are embryology (the development which takes place before birth), genetics (biological heredity), physiology (functioning of the body), and comparative biochemistry (the chemistry of living things). Their collective labors place the animal world in a chronological order—that is, a time sequence of origins—not just categories determined by the classification of structural details. This biological time table helps us to study many aspects of the evolution of man.

Physical anthropology also throws light on racial differences among men. What are racial differences? How have they arisen? Do they determine the way people behave or think? While these questions are questions for physical anthropology, those concerning people's behavior and attitude are in the wider framework of social science, involving as they do the contributions of cultural anthropology, psychology, and sociology. In physical anthropology, as in the other natural and social sciences, some of the greatest advances of recent years have been made in respect to just such questions: those for which answers must be sought through several areas of knowledge.

Another problem for physical anthropology is the nature of hereditary differences between men and the way such differences begin. How do such differences come to be established, expanded, or lost? To answer such questions physical anthropologists study human genetics, the process by which characteristic physical traits are transmitted from one generation to another. The genetics of so-called normal variations, the ordinary variations that exist among all men, such as the blood groups, is of particular concern to physical anthropologists. Blood groups may differ from individual to individual, but they are passed from parents to children in definite ways. But what probably concerns the anthropologist most about human inheritance is *population genetics*, the factors that lead to genetic stability or change in a local group of primitive men, for example.

Furthermore, physical anthropology deals with several other kinds of problems that use techniques first developed in evolutionary and racial studies. *Anthropometry*, the measurement of man, is properly a branch of physical anthropology. Man's measurement is essential in the study of growth and is also used to find and, if possible, explain variations between men that result from external influences during the growth period.

Finally, variations in human physique, whatever their cause, challenge the physical anthropologist for a description and an explanation. Sometimes the answers have practical significance as, for example, in the relation of a man's physique to his liability to become affected by one or another disease. And as man literally hems himself in, his clothes, chairs, cars, and cockpits provide a challenge for the application of physical anthropology to the design of man's world.

The Study of Man

It is usual today to divide the study of man into a series of separate though linked areas of study. *Psychology, sociology, economics, ancient history,* and *cultural anthropology*—to mention just a few of these fields—are so varied in the techniques they apply that specialists in them sometimes forget the common problems they face. Even in anthropology each scholar tends to specialize in one method of approach. The study of the history of a language is quite different from the study of the history of pottery. These, in turn, differ from the study of the history of man's anatomy. But in the end all history depends on the kind of animal man is and the way he has come to be. The biological evolution of a being who will talk and cook food in the pots he has made for that purpose is basic to the history of both language and pottery.

The differences in the cultural characteristics between the Englishman and the Eskimo, the Semite and the Seminole, the Hottentot and the Hun, can be studied only by methods of cultural history, but the very existence of culture and the occurrence of cultural differences depend on a special kind of organism with suitable brain, tongue, and vocal chords for talk and suitable hands to make pots. Only man combines both of these traits with adequate mental capacity to develop culture. The evolution of culture and of the culture bearer went on together. As man's forebears began to rely on the products of culture, he must have adapted biologically to this way of life. The further development of human capacities, and the evolution of an organism possessing them, must have depended mainly on the growth of culture itself. In many of the areas now inhabited by man it is doubtful if he could survive without clothes, shelter, and organized society. Yet he has survived and adapted, evolving in response to both the physical and cultural aspects of his environment.

2

Evolution

The Process of Change

There is no longer any doubt about the fact of evolution as the central process of nature. The theory of natural evolution is today accepted as a general principle of biology, applying equally to all forms of life. There is overwhelming evidence that the human evolved just as did the other animals. This does not, of course, exclude the possibility that at some stage in his development man has left behind him some of those traits which are more or less common to other advanced organisms that populate this globe. Man has been able to acquire other traits which distinguish him from the rest of the animal world. But we shall later see that the mechanisms that brought about this leap ahead and that continue to operate in man today are similar to the mechanisms of evolution in other organisms.

Sexual reproduction ensures that each new generation differs from the last. The relatives of a newborn infant sometimes say, "He is the image of his father." At most, however, the child merely resembles one of his parents. One never sees a child who is identical in every feature to either parent. From looking at photographs one can see that some persons look quite different from the way their parents appeared at the same age (Fig. 2-1). The changes from father to son are the very essence of evolution and provide living evidence of what has been repeated in many generations.

It is true that such differences within the family or group may be difficult to see in people foreign to us. To some ob-

Fig. 2-1. Photographs of a father and son taken in 1902 and 1942 respectively. There is great similarity in some features such as the nose, but even aside from the differences between the Russian and American uniforms it is easy to distinguish the father from the son on the basis of width of the jaw, shape of the face, and details of the region about the eyes.

servers, "All Chinese look alike." This is because the ways in which the Chinese differ from other groups of people are so easily seen that one may fail to notice the individual differences which exist between the Chinese. With suitable photographs of Chinese or Japanese, we can test the statement that there are differences from generation to generation in these peoples too. For example, the skinfold that gives the almond-eyed appearance to the Chinese has many variations and individual differences.

If it were not for such differences, however slight they may be, there could be no evolution. By *evolution* is meant any change in hereditary endowment through time. It consists of all the ways in which some inherited qualities develop and spread throughout the species while others decline or fail to be preserved. Both may go on simultaneously, while still other hereditary features may persist and pass unmodified from parents to children.

A child sometimes resembles one of his grandfathers or grandmothers but not his father or his mother. Whatever degree of resemblance he has inherited from earlier ancestors must have come to him through his parents, but the influence cannot be exactly predicted. No one knows in what member of a large family a noteworthy physical feature of a grandfather will be likely to reappear or whether it will reappear at all. Such a hereditary trait may occur in only some of the offspring, express itself to various degrees, or become modified. The process of evolution is a continuous type of change with time. It may be irregular, however. Indeed, when there are no changes whatever in environment or habits and the population does not intermarry with others, one may see merely small chance variations in physical characteristics from generation to generation without continuing evolution in one direction. In nature there are many instances of so-called living fossils such as the opossum and the horseshoe crab which have remained little modified over millions of years (Fig. 2-2). Slow evolution, however, would of necessity be rare in man and especially so in recent times with our high population mobility and changes in living conditions. We have plenty of visible proof for the fact that evolution is at work among us to produce cumulative effects of group differentiation.

Evolution through Uneven Increase in Numbers.   One example of evolution as a fact that still operates among us is the continuous change in the proportion of different groups in the population of the United States. Some groups—the American Indians, for example—have decreased in numbers. In 1600 there were close to one million in the continental United States. Now there are only about half that many.

On the other hand, certain of the immigrant groups from Europe have increased steadily as well as rapidly. Changes in the proportions of the groups that make up the world popula-

Fig. 2-2. The horseshoe crab shows little modification over millions of years.

tion likewise go on generation after generation. These populations differ genetically; hence, these changes in proportion demonstrate human evolution. One used to hear talk of a "yellow peril," the supposed result of large population increases in eastern Asia. This concept rested on an error, of course—namely, the confusion of biological and cultural values. If the high population increase of one race could be considered a threat to other races, then the peoples of Asia and Africa might have been justified in speaking of a "white peril." In the last 300 years the population of Europe has increased sixfold, and this growth rate should be doubled again to take account of increases in Europeans living outside Europe. In the same period the population of Asia has increased only fivefold and that of other parts of the world even less. This means that the average person of the physical types present in Europe 300 years ago has today several times as many living descendants as has a hypothetical average non-European man of that day. Europeans have colonized North America, Australia, New Zealand, and to lesser extents South and Central America, Africa, Asia, and Oceania. The result has been significant evolutionary change in mankind as a whole. Such change is not a problem in itself. There is no yellow peril, white peril, or black peril, although today there is a peril of excessive numbers in relation to natural resources.

Theories and Facts

But what about the long stretch of past evolution? What facts have we to demonstrate that it really took place? What human changes have occurred in the last 50,000 years? And what biological changes in the direction of the human species occupied the glacial ages of the preceding million or so years? "No one has ever found the missing link," one hears the uninformed say. By now we have much fossil evidence for all sorts of links in human ancestry. Besides skeletons of men, apes, and monkeys we have numerous fossils of a wide variety of intermediate forms, and the quantity of such finds has increased with the years. As we shall see, some of these are from apelike men, some are from manlike apes, monkeylike apes, apelike and even manlike monkeys, and there are also monkeylike lemurs, mammal-like reptiles, reptile-like amphibians, amphibian-like fishes, and other similar intermediate links between animal forms. Our problem is not in finding missing links as such. It is in establishing the genetic interrelations of fossil forms, the order in which they occur, and the way in which they lived. To solve this range of problems it is important that the search go on for specimens of more complete skeletons and variant types from different places and geologic times.

Evolution is a fact, rather than a theory. However, theories are needed to suggest explanations of facts that cannot be seen at first hand. We may describe a thousand shells on a beach and be right about the composition and shape of each shell; but to explain how they came to be there requires a theory. Not chance, but a series of events left them at the edge of the sea.

Evolution is both a history and a science. Like all sciences it collects facts and also develops theories. We need these theories to tell us how evolution works in general. In the case of man, theories help us to understand his past. The science of genetics (the study of the process of inheritance) permits us to answer the question of how human evolution could, and could not, have occurred. Thus, we may still speak of "theories of human evolution" even when we know that evolution itself is a fact.

Of great importance in the development of the theory of human evolution was the publication, over one hundred years ago, of Charles Darwin's *Origin of Species* (Fig. 2-3). In his book Darwin presented the idea of evolution through *natural selection*. This natural process, he said, causes "survival of the fittest" or continued life for those types of animals and plants best adjusted to the conditions in which they live, and death for those which are not best adjusted to these conditions. Thus, characteristics which helped man to survive spread because they were passed on from one generation to the next. Darwin's studies of animals throw light on the origin of man. Darwin and Alfred Russell Wallace, a naturalist who presented the idea of natural selection simultaneously with Darwin, at first said nothing of man. Nevertheless, critics and defenders of natural selection immediately saw that the theory could very well apply to man. In fact, twelve years after the publication of his most famous work, Darwin followed it up with, *The Descent of Man*.

Another striking event in the early history of evolutionary theory was the observation of a regular pattern of inheritance. It was originally thought that the mixing of the blood or other

American Museum of Natural History

Fig. 2-3.   Charles Darwin.

fluids caused the similarity between parents and offspring. Now we know that there is no direct mixing of bloods or other fluids. The transmission of particles (*genes*) from the parents to the offspring accounts for heredity. Gregor Mendel, who experimented with cross-breeding peas, presented his results in 1865. These, however, were never understood in his lifetime because of the boldness of his ideas and the fact that he employed methods not used in most branches of science until many decades later. The years following Mendel's experiments saw the development of knowledge of the cell and reproduction. By 1900 science was ripe for a convincing theory of genetics. Working on their own and in ignorance of Mendel's work, botanists rediscovered Mendel's principles, and others soon showed these laws to apply to heredity in man.

By the early 1900's the theory of evolution had become a fact, soon to be supported by fossil finds and an understanding of the principles of human genetics.

3

The Biological Basis of Life

Chromosomes and Genes

Before exploring the facts of human evolution, we should know how that process works in the rest of the animal kingdom. This will help us to interpret man's own history. All life shares some properties, and we may best begin with some species quite unlike our own. We shall start with the origin of the simplest forms of life and progress toward man's "poor relations," the monkeys and apes.

Few scientists today deny that man could have evolved from non-human animals. There is plenty of fossil evidence that this did take place. Likewise, it can be shown that all but the simplest organic forms could have evolved from simpler ones. The other fact we need to explain evolution is evidence that some unit of life is capable of producing an exact image of itself with all the original functions. It is necessary that such images will sometimes be slightly inexact in one way or another. These inexact images must, in turn, be capable of reproducing themselves.

The nuclei of cells contain particles that tend to absorb certain dye pigments; thus stained they can be seen under the microscope. When cells are undergoing division (mitosis), the deeply stained particles are seen to be small elongated bodies. A species usually has a definite number of these rodlike bodies, called *chromosomes* (Fig. 3-1). Particular segments of chromosomes are concerned with the transmission and development of particular hereditary traits or characteristics. These

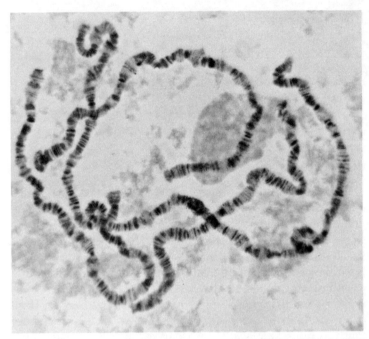

General Biological Supply House

Fig. 3-1.   Giant chromosomes from the salivary gland of a fruit fly.

segments, too small to be seen through a microscope, are called *genes*. The gene is essential to evolution: It can produce an image of itself, and the image is occasionally inexact.

All current definitions of the gene agree in considering it to be that segment of chromosomal material which is essential for the chemical synthesis of a particular substance. The genes determine the exact chemical composition and arrangement of the molecules synthesized by the organism. Although this only describes what the gene does, we shall indicate something of what the gene is when we describe the nature of the complex organic compounds (chemical compounds containing carbon atoms) that constitute the genes.

Chemical Evolution of Organic Compounds. How could the materials present in the world before life existed produce such complex organic compounds? So far as we know, the naturally occurring complex organic compounds of today are the results of life processes: Life seems always to be dependent on prior life. Imagine, however, a time when there was no life—a time, that is, when there was no process by which, after death, complex organic compounds were regularly reduced to simpler forms. The rot, decay, and fermentation that reduce organic compounds to simpler compounds and chemical elements can occur only as a result of the life processes of microorganisms. The simpler substances of alcohol and vinegar derive from plant starches and sugars by organic fermentation. Similarly, yeasts, molds, or bacteria are needed to decompose flesh or plant fibers to water and simple gases. Without fermentation the grape would keep forever. Nonfermenting grapes never existed, however, because yeasts, molds, and bacteria evolved before the vine.

Since until there was life there was nothing to cause compounds to decay, compounds would have tended to become more complex, not simpler. We assume that one of these complex compounds achieved the status of an organism, able to reproduce copies of itself. What we call life began with this substance, as it used and broke down the surrounding substances for the creation of its descendants.

According to one scientist, the simple chemicals of which the original atmosphere of the earth was composed could, in the presence of electric energy such as would be provided by lightning, produce compounds which, in turn, could lead to the formation of *amino acids*, the chemical "building blocks" that are found in all forms of life. Whether the transformations demonstrated by this scientist's experiments represent what actually happened cannot now be determined, but lightning or ultraviolet energy from the sun could have effected the first steps of such a chemical synthesis in which a complex compound is built up from simpler ones.

All theories of the natural origin of life claim that some form of intense energy—light, heat, radioactivity, ultraviolet irradiation, or electricity—converted simple one-carbon compounds into chemical compounds with multiple carbon atoms. Laboratory experiments have shown several methods of bringing about this process.

Continued application of energy would lead to even more complex carbon compounds. Some of these compounds would have the special property of causing these chemical changes to occur at a faster rate of speed. Other processes, such as crystallization, determine special arrangements of molecules. These processes would have started an orderly system of change in organic compounds.

The Origin of Life. Proteins are still more complex than amino acids. They consist of combinations of these acids and are present in all plants and animals. Every living thing must either synthesize proteins or live on organisms which do. Even the simplest plants are capable of several stages of synthesis. Until life began, the nonliving environment could have held quite complex substances, for there would have been no life to break down such compounds by decay. Once, however, any complex of carbon-containing molecules was able to reproduce itself, it would be alive, but its descendants would begin to use up all the natural chemical food on which they grew. If some descendant were modified (mutated) in the direction of being able to grow on some simpler substance, this form would have an advantage and would multiply in a world in which the original "food for life" had become scarce.

Each time this happened the descendants added a new capacity to synthesize and, at the same time, the world lost some complex organic substance achieved by non-life processes. The gap between the most complex nonorganic substances and the simplest forms of life increased. The gap could hardly have been jumped by a single event; many steps were probably involved, so that what were originally chemical syntheses began to take place within the organism. They became biological processes.

The distinction between what took place within the organism and what went on outside was an essential step. We cannot conceive of life as a property of a homogeneous fluid. From the start there must have been some structure which prevented the products of the essential chemical reactions from being washed away. That is, living things are composed of one or more cells. Biological cells have walls which confine. Cohesiveness and a tendency to produce walls would have permitted much more effective chemical interaction. The biological system must have developed these properties very early.

The Capacity to Reproduce

All types of living things possess one property not shared by nonliving objects. That is, given the right environment, they can create essentially identical images of themselves. As one of the essential qualities of living matter is reproduction, the essential quality of the offspring must include this same capacity to reproduce. Our knowledge of how reproduction takes place has been increased by a series of experiments on minute organisms such as the bread mold, *Neurospora*. In these experiments it is seen that the units of heredity, the genes, appear to act through *enzymes*, organic chemicals that serve to speed up certain chemical reactions. It was fairly obvious in theory, even before it could be demonstrated, that the genes must have a structure exactly paralleled in the enzymes. Unlike those of enzymes, however, the molecules of genes, or as we shall see, series of them, can serve as templates or molds for the production of more of their own kind. But as well as acting as molds to reproduce themselves, genes act as molds to produce corresponding enzymes that speed up important biochemical syntheses in the tissues without themselves being altered in the process.

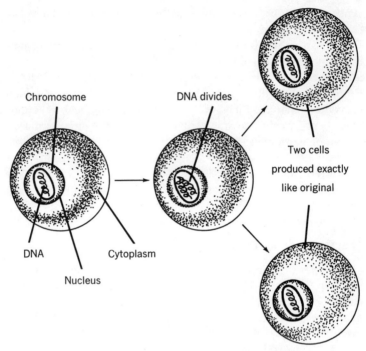

Fig. 3-2.   DNA dividing during the process of cell division.

The Role of DNA.   On the basis of experiments on the chemistry of the smallest parts of cells—the new science of cytochemistry—Watson and Crick have constructed a picture of the material of life. They see the essential material as being in a substance called *deoxyribonucleic acid,* which they call DNA for short.

DNA is found in the chromosomes of the nucleus of virtually every living cell and does not ordinarily occur elsewhere. It is a giant molecule millions of times as heavy as hydrogen, which is the lightest atom known. A DNA molecule, however, is so thin that it cannot be seen even through an electron microscope. The DNA molecule is coiled up inside the chromosome (Fig. 3-2). Although only one coil of DNA is shown, there are probably hundreds of these molecules in every chromosome. DNA has two functions. The first function is to pass hereditary information, the biological "instructions," from parents to their offspring. The second is to control the formation of proteins everywhere in the body.

Hydrogen, oxygen, carbon, nitrogen, and *phosphorus* are the five common chemical elements that compose the DNA molecule. These elements are arranged in different chemical groups in two long chains. These chains consist of alternate sugar and phosphate groups. Cross links hold the two chains together. These links are called nucleotide base bars. Thousands of these cross links may be found in one DNA molecule.

The question remains as to how DNA functions in heredity. Each time a DNA molecule divides it produces two new molecules exactly like the original one (see Fig. 3-2). Watson and Crick have offered an explanation of how this occurs. They reasoned that in order to fit together into a chain, a special relation must exist among the four groups present in the base bars. Under normal conditions all base bars would have to be the same length. Only two types of pairs can match in length and each of these two types can occur in either of two positions. The order and position of the pairs represents genetic information. The many possible arrangements along the length of the chain provide the key for the codes of inheritance unique to every species and to the individuals within the species (Fig. 3-3). When the DNA molecule divides, each spiral comes apart at the bonds between the pairs. It is not known exactly how this takes place, but one half must "unscrew" from the other or they must break apart at each turn. Very possibly only a section of the double chain comes apart at a time. The process goes down the spiral as the code is "read." The image may be formed a bit at a time. Each of the pair of molecules produces two complete and identical spirals where only one existed before. The DNA does not produce an exact image of itself, but a reverse image. Each half

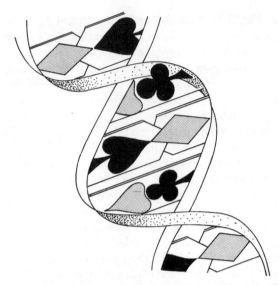

Fig. 3-3. DNA's four nucleotides, here represented as the four suits in a deck of cards, are arranged in a fixed order that is unique for each individual. However, diamonds can pair only with spades and clubs only with hearts.

builds a new opposite, making two new molecules exactly like the original one with the same order of base pairs. The whole material is reproduced, and the result is two identical chromosomes, each usually capable of making further copies.

The DNA of the chromosomes has another function too. It must control the formation of the specific proteins determined by its ancestry. It does this by imprinting its message sequence on a substance called RNA which transports it to the tiny protein factories within the cells. There, RNA acts to determine the sequence in which amino acids are strung together to form the protein. It would take three bases of RNA, called a triplet, to determine an amino acid. A succession of triplets, each determining an amino acid, thus strings together the amino acids in a definite order determined by the order of the triplets in the RNA. The structure of the protein formed in this way therefore is exactly the same every time the same coded message is "read." The efforts of scientists to break the genetic code have been furthered by experiments with RNA in which every base is identical. This kind of synthetic RNA determined the production of a protein that consisted of chains of a single kind of amino acid. Many steps in the decoding still remain unsolved. Experimental evidence suggests that different triplets may lead to the incorporation of the same amino acid in a protein. Furthermore, we are not sure whether the code is identical in all organisms. Experiments with synthetic RNA containing some but not all of the four kinds of bases are closing the gap, however.

Human Genetics

We shall now raise the question: *"How* has man evolved?" In considering this question we shall want to limit ourselves to the properties of men that are biologically transmitted from generation to generation. Biological inheritance is sometimes affected by culture. For instance, the selection of a mate is a cultural factor that may influence heredity. The further a group of humans evolves culturally, the larger this influence. The fields of cultural anthropology and history deal with the cultural influences on man. Our discussion of cultural influences, however, will be limited to their effects on human genetics.

Variability. Anyone who looks about him will see that people differ. They even differ, to some degree, from their mothers, fathers, brothers, and sisters. Some of these differences are caused by the process of heredity. Although it is true that occasionally a pair of brothers or a pair of sisters are born essentially identical in heredity (identical twins), this exception only calls attention to the variability of man in general.

Hereditary variability between people seems always to have been great. Wherever several fossil skeletons are found in a

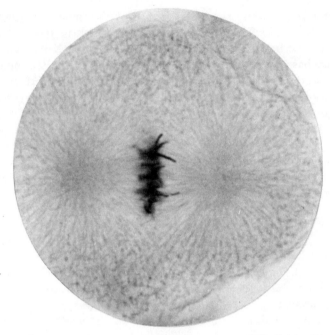

Fig. 3-4. During metaphase the pairs of chromosomes are lined up along the center of the cells.

single place and belonging to the same time they vary somewhat. Another evidence of the variability of the forerunners of man is the fact that individuals among all other animals also vary.

Human Chromosomes. During cell division (*mitosis*), chromosomes double the number of their strands, split in two, and half go to form each of the two daughter cells. This leaves each new cell with the same number of chromosomes as the parent cell. The moment just before cell division is called *metaphase* (intermediate stage). Cells killed and stained at this stage can be seen in the microscope to contain pairs of chromosomes (Fig. 3-4).

It was long believed that in man there are always 48 chromosomes in cells of body tissues. Recently the question of the number of human chromosomes has been restudied. This restudy has been made by the new techniques of tissue culture. *Tissue culture* is the technique by means of which cells can be grown in a suitable medium outside the body. Cells which reach metaphase can be prevented from developing further by suitable chemical treatment. Material from tissue culture with many metaphase cells can be squashed so that the cells are spread out and the chromosomes can be photographed through a microscope. Images of the chromosomes in the photograph can then be cut apart and mounted for counting and study. Counts of human chromosomes using these improved methods reveal 46 per cell with rare examples of abnormal numbers. The 46 chromosomes usually present consist of 23 pairs. Although indistinguishable through the microscope, the two chromosomes of a pair are not identical. That is, although two corresponding genes may control eye color, one chromosome may contain the gene for blue eyes and the other may contain the gene for brown eyes. We then say the individual is *heterozygous* for eye color. If each chromosome contains corresponding genes which are exactly alike (in this case both chromosomes would contain genes for blue eyes or both chromosomes would contain genes for brown eyes), we say the individual is *homozygous* for eye color. The chromosomes differ in the genes for every characteristic for which the individual is *heterozygous*.

Sex-differentiating Chromosomes.   Twenty-two of the 23 pairs of chromosomes are matched in length and shape. In the human male, and in that of most other animals, the other pair consists of one long and one short chromosome. The longer chromosome of the pair is called the X chromosome and the shorter one, the Y chromosome. Both are called *sex-differentiating* chromosomes. The male has one X and one Y chromosome; the female has two X chromosomes and hence has 23 matched pairs (Fig. 3-5).

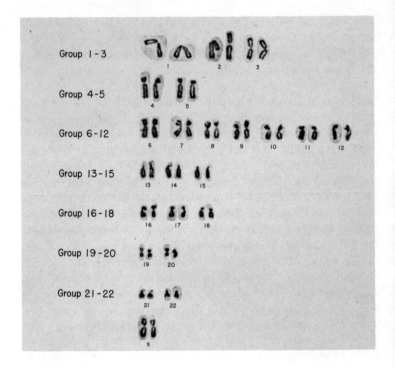

Courtesy of Dr. E. Powsner

Fig. 3-5.   Microphotographs of the 22 pairs and X chromosomes of
a normal female cell cut apart and remounted matched for form and
size. In the normal male there would be an X and Y chromosome
instead of two X chromosomes.

The sex cells involved in reproduction, the *spermatozoa* or
sperm of the male and *ova* or egg of the female, develop in a
special manner. As they mature they divide twice, and in one
of these divisions they do not duplicate their chromosomes.
In this way, the egg or sperm gets only one of each pair of
chromosomes. The total number of chromosomes in the sex
cell of humans is, therefore, 23. In the reproductive process
the mature sperm and the mature egg fuse to produce a cell

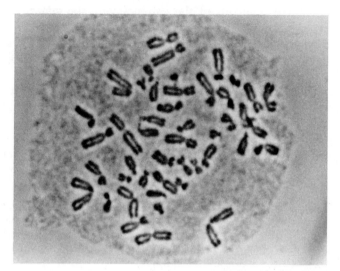

Courtesy of Dr. E. Powsner

Fig. 3-6. Untreated bone-marrow cell undergoing mitosis. There is clear representation of 46 chromosomes of this human female cell.

with the complete number of chromosomes, 46. The offspring thus receives one chromosome of each pair from the father and one from the mother.

Since women have two X chromosomes, a child must always receive an X chromosome from its mother, and its sex is, therefore, determined by whether it receives an X or a Y chromosome from its father. The offspring who inherit the father's X chromosome will have two X chromosomes and be female. Those who inherit his Y chromosome will have an unmatched XY pair and be male.

Mendel's Principles

Most of the variation within a single species is not the result of differences in whole chromosomes as in the case of sex, however. As we have seen, variation depends on the much more limited segments of the chromosomes, the genes. Long before the physical basis for the gene and the base sequence of DNA was even suspected, breeding experiments with plants and animals had already revealed how the genes work. Beginning in 1856, Gregor Johann Mendel had bred different varieties of peas in the small garden of an Augustinian monastery in what is now Czechoslovakia. Mendel discovered that when he crossbred peas which contrast in some characteristic, the cross-bred heterozygote was indistinguishable from one of the parent types. The trait which thus shows up in heterozygotic form is called *dominant*. That the gene for the other parental type (called *recessive*) is also present in the hybrid can be demonstrated by breeding hybrids with hybrids. Offspring which receive the recessive gene from both parents and have it on both of a pair of chromosomes show the recessive trait even though the parents, who each had the trait on only one of the pair of chromosomes, do not.

By a series of experiments of this sort Mendel and others have demonstrated how inheritance works. Genes on different chromosomes are inherited independently and the offspring of a single pair of parents may inherit different combinations of the parents' genes. Furthermore, through the working of recessive inheritance, children may inherit characteristics which have never shown up in the parents.

4

Population Genetics

The Breeding Population

Darwin's main contribution to the understanding of evolution is the theory of *natural selection*. This theory states that, of two slightly different plants or animals, the one whose inherited characteristics better adapt it to life under a given set of circumstances has the better chance of leaving offspring. This is true whether or not the competing organisms belong to the same group, so long as they are living the same kind of life in the same place. Natural selection not only means "the survival of the survivors;" it also implies that, on the average, a new generation composed of the offspring of such survivors will be more fit than the last generation. Since the new generation is descended from the fittest members of the previous generation, evolution favors the genetically fit. Much evidence has confirmed this theory.

In the last 30 years or more, however, scientists have applied genetics to the analysis of evolution. According to the theory of evolution which combines natural selection and genetics, one should define as "evolutionary" any event that alters the frequency with which specific genes occur in a new generation. Any circumstance that causes a group to change in gene frequencies, systematically generation after generation, is, by definition, a significant factor in the evolution of the group. The development of particular combinations of genes may be the most significant form of evolution, but this is merely a special case. Simultaneous changes in several gene frequencies must stem from the same basic causes as change in the frequency of a single gene in the group.

It is difficult to define the group in human populations. In man, religion, caste, race, economic status, education, class, and other factors affect the selection of mates, hence the social groups which the geneticist would call "breeding isolates." Before we can study ongoing evolution in man, we must define such subgroups. The *breeding group* may be thought of as that social group within which mates are ordinarily sought and found. It is bound together by marriage within the group and hence shares a "pool" of genes. The ways in which the gene frequencies of such a group may be altered are *mutation, natural selection, random genetic drift*, and *degree of isolation*. Evolution may be defined as *the change in gene frequencies resulting from the interaction of these four factors*.

Before discussing gene frequency changes, we should first clear up one common fallacy: Dominant genes do not become more frequent at the expense of recessive ones. In the absence of other factors, gene frequencies in a population will remain the same from generation to generation. The terms "dominant" and "recessive" refer to the mode of inheritance. The dominant and recessive genes are *alleles* (they occupy the same location on the chromosome, like the genes for blue and brown eyes). Dominant merely means that when a gene so described is paired with its recessive allele in an individual, the dominant gene will determine the outward appearance (the *phenotype*). The likelihood of the recessive gene being transmitted is not reduced. In other words, a child has an equal chance of inheriting any of the genes of each parent—be they dominant or recessive. For example, two parents of blood group A both carrying the gene for A (the dominant) and the gene for O (the recessive) will transmit, on the average, as many genes for O as for A to their offspring. However, the genes for O will be indicated by the blood grouping test only if there are two in the same individual, one inherited from each parent.

There is an apparent difference in respect to sex: The sexes, themselves genetically determined, are not born in equal numbers. More males are born than females; in the United States, for example, approximately 105 boys are born for every 100 girls. Of course, the difference does not progress from generation to generation. More males die young, marry late, or remain bachelors. The ratio of the sexes thus remains constant.

Mutation. The first of the four ways in which gene frequencies can change, in fact the only way in which totally new possibilities arise, is through change in the genetic material—a change that can be transmitted. Several varieties of such changes have been observed in the chromosomes and genes of plants and animals. The most important from the evolutionary viewpoint is the change that occurs in a single gene—that is, *gene mutation.* A gene mutation can be defined as a spontaneous change at a single point on a chromosome (perhaps only one or a few cross links of DNA) rather than an alteration of a whole chromosome or a large segment of it.

So far no one has been able to predict which genes will mutate nor the direction mutations will take, although mutations can be greatly increased in frequency by some chemicals, such as mustard gas, and especially by X ray and other types of radiation.

Mutations are generally disadvantageous from the standpoint of survival—for the simple reason that the form or organ that changes is already the outcome of a chain of natural selection for fitness that reaches far into the past. The established genes, therefore, are quite advantageous. Nevertheless, the capacity to mutate (but at a low rate) is itself selectively advantageous. With a changing environment a species may be able to tolerate disadvantageous mutations for the sake of an occasional advantageous one. The possibility of change and its occurrence in one individual or a few individuals prevents the whole evolutionary line from facing extinction. This may explain why mutation is an attribute of all living things. The rates of mutation in man and other animals are normally between 5 and 50 per million births. Some such rate may be the most favorable, naturally established through selection.

Recently, concern has been expressed on the genetic effects

of fallout from testing of radioactive weapons. Most mutations are harmful, as we have noted, and each increase in
radioactivity tends to increase the rate of mutation in man.
Therefore, as one geneticist has put it, we are increasing "our
load of mutations." If this increase is minor, natural selection
(through death and sterility of *mutants*, the carriers of mutations) can probably keep our species alive. There is, however,
some disagreement among experts as to what can safely be
considered "minor." Actually, there is no set limit. There is no
way to predict accurately the genetic effect on mankind of
hydrogen-bomb experiments, discharge of waste from atomic-
energy installations, or the widespread medical use of X rays.
So far we have probably raised human mutation rates relatively little, but we have no safe way of counting "moderate"
increases in undesirable recessive mutations or of appraising
their possible long-run effects. Any penetrating radiation that
reaches the ovaries or testes is capable of producing inheritable mutations in sex cells. The number of such mutations is
greater the longer and more intense the exposure to such radiation. But, again, we have no way of predicting exactly which
cells will mutate or what mutations will occur.

Natural Selection. Natural selection, the second factor in
evolution, is clearly important in modifying whole species. In
some situations, for example where antelope and lions live in
the same region, faster species of antelope have had better
chances to survive than slower types. Furthermore, the work-
ings of natural selection in man can clearly be seen in some
cases where it tends to maintain a genetic trait in the population. Thus, sickle-cell disease is a serious hereditary condition
which is known to occur only in individuals whose ancestors
lived for many generations in areas where malaria was prevalent. It turns out that heterozygous individuals (that is, those
who inherit the gene for sickling from one parent and who
receive the normal allele from the other parent) have a greater
resistance to malaria. The probability that some individuals
will inherit two genes for sickle-cell disease (one from each

parent) and have the disease is the price mankind pays for having a gene which, when on only one chromosome, protects its carrier against malaria.

Serious doubt remains, however, concerning the nature of the evolutionary origin of most of the differences between human races. It is not easy to find examples of natural selection at work in modern races. We can only guess what advantages to survival in given circumstances there may be in blond human hair, or dark skin, for instance.

Most of the information about the role played by natural selection (selection pressure) in respect to human traits is obtained by studying traits that are either nearly universal or very rare in the species; that is, the genes responsible for normal development of sight, hearing, growth, and so on, and those causing major impairments: blindness, deafness, dwarfism, and the like. In spite of this situation, much guessing has been done concerning almost every human racial trait. Thus, some anthropologists have argued that differences in body shape in the races of various parts of the world are related to climatic differences, especially with regard to extreme climatic regions and their peoples: the Eskimos, the Australian aborigines, nomads of the Sahara, and tropical Africans.

During his voyage on the *Beagle*, Darwin saw some nearly naked natives on the shore of the cold barren island of Tierra del Fuego, at the southernmost tip of South America. If he had known then that one native group, the Yahgan, are, on the average, extremely short, while another, the Ona, living nearby on the same island, are tall—how would he have explained the situation as survival of the fittest? Similarly, how can one explain the differences in body type between the American Indians from the dry regions of the southwestern United States and the desert peoples of North Africa and Arabia?

One possible answer is that one or the other of these two groups was not native to the region it now occupies. It might have evolved elsewhere and migrated recently into the region.

In these cases we have no direct knowledge of such migrations. The populations which are compared may both have occupied the climatic zone for about the same length of time. After the fact one may argue that this or that attribute of physique must be good for this or that climate. Such an argument, however, starts by assuming the theory of natural selection of racial characteristics. As long as other possible explanations remain untested, the argument does little to support the theory. Factors in cultural history, such as the use of clothes or weapons, may be the chief influences in the distribution of races. Although arguments relating racial difference and climate are interesting, scientists, for the most part, must still label them as "undemonstrated."

Random Genetic Drift. Random genetic drift is the third of the four main ways by which changes in gene frequency are explained. If mutation and natural selection do not adequately account for human evolution, what else could cause it? One suggestion is that, in part, it may be a result of chance. This explanation seems a contradiction in terms: Saying that changes are due to chance seems to be saying that they are not explained. What is implied in this case, however, is merely that some chance factors, unrelated to biology, increase or decrease gene frequency. Thus, if the Spanish armada had conquered the British, genes for blue eyes might well be rarer in the United States today. Likewise, by chance, a couple with brown eyes may have children while their neighbors with blue eyes do not. Factors of no direct relation to genetics may change gene frequencies, although this would not prevent a complete explanation if it were possible and worthwhile to obtain all the unknown or doubtful factors. The total effect of haphazard variations is called *random genetic drift.*

It should be apparent that the smaller the population, the more likely are such chance fluctuations. In large groups they are not likely to be a significant factor. The total size of the breeding population is important, but so are the differences in the size of families. Obviously, if many individuals had few or no offspring, while others were the parents of many, random genetic drift would be more prevalent than if the distribution of offspring were more even. In a jungle tribe where half the adult women are wives of the chief, genes he carries may increase in the group. Great variability in family size thus has the same kind of effect as decrease in size of the group.

Isolation. Another factor besides mutation, natural selection, and random genetic drift may influence gene frequency. Mating is selective; there is a tendency for members of subgroups of the species to mate among themselves (isolation) and occasionally to interbreed. If the groups differ greatly in their gene frequencies, then a mate of one's own group is more likely to share one's own genetic characteristics than is a mate from another group. Isolation of groups causes males of a particular kind to usually breed with females of the same kind. Men and women are most likely to marry persons in the same area or country. Similarly, human beings usually marry members of their own social group—those who share the same values and speak the same language and like the same things.

Some human breeding groups are small enough for random factors to be quite pronounced. The population of the Bass Straight Islands, Australia, started with 21 adults. The 200-odd persons who, until a recent volcanic eruption forced them to leave, inhabited the little island of Tristan de Cunha in the South Atlantic are descended from eight men and seven women and a few later immigrants. Pitcairn Island in the Pacific was peopled by the descendants of six of the mutineers of the British ship *Bounty* and eight or nine Polynesian women. These populations have remained relatively isolated for many generations and each of them shares distinct physical characteristics.

Race

As we have seen, the pool of human inherited characteristics differs from place to place and changes from time to time. A description of this situation in terms of fixed categories called *races* is obviously an inexact approach. It is preferable to deal with racial characteristics in terms of the history of groups of people and the corresponding modifications in their *gene pool*, as the sum of the genes of the members of a breeding population is called. There are, of course, some differences between some of the peoples of the major land masses of the world, although all sorts of intermediate populations also exist. Even these local groups usually differ from each other *on the average* in respect to some physical characteristics. They also differ in the proportion of individuals with different physiological and biochemical characteristics. The fact of such differences between populations has been misused to imply that there is scientific evidence bearing on the question of "superiority" of one race over another. The fact is, however, that questions of mentality and temperament are so complex that even if populations differ in their inherited shares of these, results of intelligence tests and the like do not demonstrate it. Although differences do occur in the average performance on tests of various kinds in populations of various places, no satisfactory evidence of essential racial differences of this kind has been secured. The differences in experience of the members of the populations examined always interfere with a genetic interpretation. Furthermore, in studies in which the differences in experience are minimized the differences in test performances also tend to be small. It is logical to believe that people whose ancestors have long lived in a particular environment and way of life may have adapted to these circumstances. Experiments with the way people respond to cold suggest that this is a case of adaptation to climate. The aboriginals of Australia, for instance, show a decrease in the temperature of the skin of their feet when they sleep out in the cold, thus conserving body warmth in the trunk, whereas other peoples, including Eskimos, tend to increase their heat output and require more food. But the best adaptation to cold is the presence of clothing, shelter, and other equipment. Today the biological differences are probably less relevant, since man everywhere has evolved under natural selection pressures different from those which may now be important. A tendency to lower mutation rates under a given amount of irradiation may now be more important, even in Australia, than the capacity to sleep with cold toes.

Mutation, natural selection (in respect to both the physical and the cultural environments), random genetic drift, and isolation have led to differences in the gene pools of groups of men. One may, therefore, deal with such groups as races for the purpose of tracing their biological history. Such races resemble each other in some characteristics but differ in others. Furthermore, there are often gradual changes in gene frequencies from place to place. Therefore, analysis of the distribution of particular biological differences gives a more accurate description of the human species (even for purposes of tracing the biological history of various populations) than a categorization of peoples in terms of race. Even physical prowess, such as that needed by athletes, depends on individual physique, training, and attitude. The genetic components of these are so nearly independent of race that studies of athletes, for instance, do not convincingly relate differences in performance to the race of the subjects. That a few American Negroes have excelled in running and boxing is probably because our society opens avenues to success for different social groups in different ways. Some non-Negroes who might have the physiques to break world records in the sprints are encouraged by social pressures to devote their attention to other activities. In the same way, as opportunities open up, an increasing number of American Negroes find that they have the skills and interest to seek an education for the professions. It is difficult to see how the biological component in success in these activities could be related to the kinds of biological differences we now find between populations. At least such relationships have not been demonstrated.

5

Man in the Animal Kingdom

Among the living things, those which require organic food and oxygen for respiration are called *animals*. Their movements are in response to outside stimuli; that is, animals have feelings and, although it is difficult for us to know how they feel, we can see that they respond rapidly to stimuli. Man is, in this sense, an animal: He moves and feels. The animals range from tiny one-celled organisms to very complex beings. A feature of the animal kingdom—which all animals use in some generations and some (including man) use in all generations—is *bisexual reproduction*. That is, reproduction is not simply the production of an image of one parent but the combination of characteristics inherited from two parents.

In bisexual reproduction the chromosomes are paired. Each member of the pair may have different genes. It is a chance matter which of a pair of chromosomes will recombine during reproduction. In bisexual reproduction, therefore, offspring will differ from each other and from each parent. Bisexual reproduction thus provides for great variability.

Throughout evolution increasingly complex types of organisms have evolved. There have been a number of giant steps such as the development of mobility, the ability to go after food instead of having to live on what happens to drift by. Such giant steps may be thought of as advances in the sense that they are accompanied by increased complexity within the animal itself. The increase in number of functions requires greater differentiation of structures. After each such major modification has been attained, the organisms which possess it

43

have not only increased in numbers but also in kinds. This subsequent diversification of a major type into species adapted to various aspects of the environment is called *radiation*.

Each level in the animal kingdom has a special name, beginning with races (or subspecies) and going up to grades. Thus, animals whose bodies are made up of more than one cell, and in which different cells perform different functions, form a major division of the animal kingdom, a separate grade from the one-celled animals.

Chordates

The major division of grades are called *phyla* (singular, *phylum*, meaning branch). Among multicelled animals man belongs to the phylum of the *chordates*. These animals are bilaterally symmetrical. That is, the left and right sides of the animal are mirror images of one another. They are distinguished by having, at some time during their life, a flexible cord, the notochord (from the Greek word *noton*, the back, where the notochord is always located). They also have a spinal cord; but it is the notochord, not the spinal chord that distinguishes the Phylum Chordata.

Of the chordates, the most numerous group shares still other features with man. This subphylum is the *vertebrates* and includes the fishes, amphibians, reptiles, birds, and mammals. These forms have a spinal cord with a brain at one end. The cord and the brain form the central nervous system, which coordinates movement and sensation. In addition, vertebrates have a well-developed vertebral column (the spine) to surround and protect the spinal cord. They also have an internal skeleton of bone or cartilage which surrounds and protects such organs as the brain and sense organs, and enables the limb to support the body. The vertebrates regularly have locomotor appendages. Except for certain fish, these always consist of two pairs of limbs or, as in snakes and whales, some evidence of descent from animals which had them.

Classification of Man in the Animal Kingdom

Grade	*Metazoa.* Including all multicelled animals.
Phylum	*Chordata.* Including animals with notochords and gill slits.
Subphylum	*Vertebrata.* Including fishes, amphibians, reptiles, and birds.
Class	*Mammalia.* Including marsupials and egg-laying mammals.
Subclass	*Eutheria.* Including rodents, Carnivores, etc.
Order	*Primates.* Including tarsiers, lemurs, and tree shrews.
Suborder	*Anthropoidea.* Including the Old and New World monkeys.
Superfamily	*Hominoidea.* Including the great apes and gibbons.
Family	*Hominidae.* Including all tool-making forms of fossil primates.
Genus	*Homo.* Including Java Man, Peking Man, Neandertal Man, Rhodesian Man, and Solo Man.
Species	*Homo sapiens* (present day man). Including all post-glacial men.

Mammals. Subdivisions of phyla are called *classes* by biologists. One is the class Mammalia (having mammae, breasts). Animals within this distinct category of vertebrates have breasts and nourish their young with milk. Because *mammals* nourish their young after birth, they establish social relations between female and offspring. Social relations, characteristic of the whole class, are especially useful to the mammal *man* for the generation-to-generation transmission of culture through learning. Mammals are warm-blooded animals. This means that the body temperature is internally controlled. Mammals can, therefore, remain active in cold weather. The body temperature of some mammals changes somewhat, but even the bear during hibernation does not undergo a slowing of body processes to the extent characteristic of fishes or reptiles similarly exposed to the cold. In cold environments mammals, therefore, manage better than reptiles; no crocodiles and few varieties of lizards and snakes are found outside the tropics. In addition, mammals are the only animals with hair. This hair is lacking or reduced in the adult of some giant forms of mammals, such as the whale and the elephant.

Within the class Mammalia are three so-called subclasses. The first is that of the mammals that, in common with reptiles and birds, lay eggs as their mode of reproduction. The duck-billed platypus and the spiny anteater, both of Australia and the latter also of New Guinea, are the only two mammals belonging to this subclass. These egg-laying mammals are called *monotremes*.

The *marsupials* form a second subclass of mammals. This group includes the kangaroo, the "teddy-bear" koala, and also the American opossum. Marsupials are *viviparous*; that is, they give birth to their young. The newborn are very dependent, however, and must find their way to a pouch on the mother's abdomen.

Man belongs to the third subclass, *Eutheria*, mammals which develop by a special process in which the egg is shed from the mother's ovary, is fertilized, and then attaches itself into the walls of the mother's womb. The *embryo*—the early stage of development of the organism—produces a disc (placenta) on the wall of the womb. This disc of tissue permits interchange of fluids between mother and offspring. Hence, this subclass consists of the placental animals. While the bird's or reptile's egg must contain yolk enough to nourish the embryo until it hatches, as well as provide for storing the waste products of the developing embryo, the placental mammal uses the body mechanisms of the adult mother for these functions and for supplying oxygen to the tissues of the embryo. In this way the offspring can be protected until more fully developed.

6

The Order Primates

What are the Primates?

The study of the mammals is especially important to human evolution because one order of eutherian (placental) mammals, the *primates,* is made up of those groups, living or extinct, with which man shares some of his outstanding traits. It is difficult to define the primates. They have collarbones, rings of bone about the eyes, and freely movable thumbs or first toes, but each of these characteristics is shared with some other animals.

The primates are an ancient group. Although we may think of our kind as highly developed, the primates are primitive; in many respects they retain generalized mammalian features and have evolved less than other orders. This very primitiveness is one of the reasons why the primates have few features distinguishing them from certain mammals of other orders. Instead, primates are perhaps best distinguished by certain tendencies that are more marked in some than in other members of the order. These include reduced number of young born at a time and a corresponding reduction in number of mammary glands; keen vision; grasping hands, and, sometimes, feet; and, most important of all, high development of certain parts of the brain, especially the so-called grey matter which is responsible for conscious functions. A discussion of other primates will set the stage for a study of man's place in this order.

Any system of classification must be based on degrees of similarity. The question is, similarity in respect to what? The

New York Zoological Society

Fig. 6-1.   Ring-tailed lemur of Madagascar.

answer of biologists who make such classifications is: similarity in respect to traits that best show common origins. One cannot always identify such traits, but those who study the fossils will take extinct as well as living forms into account in their scheme and thus have a richer material for classification. We can start with the most widely used set of names for various animals, but we will also mention some new evidence that will slightly alter this scheme.

The "Pre-monkeys" or Prosimians.   The lemurs of Madagascar (Fig. 6-1) are, perhaps, the most characteristic of the surviving members of Prosimians or "Pre-monkeys," but they are also among the primates least closely related to monkeys.

Fig. 6-2.   The loris has large eyes for night vision.

Some of the other pre-monkeys are also specialized for particular modes of life. One type from Madagascar, the Aye-aye, has peculiar ratlike front teeth and claws which permit it to gnaw and claw open limbs of trees in search of grubs which it holds on its spindly middle finger. The little mouse lemur sleeps the summer through while nourishing itself from a special fat pad at the base of the tail. The Lorises and related forms of Asia and Africa (Fig. 6-2) are given to night prowling for insect prey, and the tarsier of the Philippines and Borneo apparently lives entirely in this way. Although the tarsier (Fig. 6-3) is equipped with elongated feet, to give it spring when jumping, and enormous eyes relative to its small body,

New York Zoological
Society Photo

Fig. 6-3. Tarsiers have eyes that look to the front. This is a characteristic found in "higher" primates.

a number of details of his anatomy are similar to those of
"higher" primates: The organs of smell are reduced, while
those of sight are emphasized. As in man and the owls, the
eyes look to the front rather than to either side—as in the
horse. Carriage horses are equipped with blinders to compel
forward vision, but horses have not evolved the two-eyed view
of tarsier and many other primates.

The lemur-like tree shrews (Fig. 6-4) were at first not even
considered to be primates. They resemble the insectivores, the
mammalian order which includes the tiny true shrews, especially in the anatomy of the skeleton, but the composition of

their blood serum and some anatomical details place the tree shrews clearly among the primates. The very primitiveness of both the primates and the Insectivora—the slowness of their evolution in most respects—should lead one to expect that small forms of each might resemble one another.

Suborder: Anthropoidea

The rest of the primates, the suborder *Anthropoidea*, consist of the monkeys, apes, and man.

The Monkeys of Central and South America. Although members of this suborder have much in common with one another, the monkeys of Central and South America—the New World monkeys—are clearly distinct from the rest in that they have an extra premolar tooth on each side of each jaw, and the nostrils of some species are relatively wide apart. The New World monkeys also vary among themselves in structure and habits. The little marmosets retain a pre-monkey tendency to have litters, usually giving birth to twins, whereas the rest of the Anthropoidea usually have their young one at a time. Marmosets eat both animal and vegetable food: Their diet includes some live insects, grubs, and spiders. Another

New York Zoological Society Photo

Fig. 6 4.   Tree shrew, a small, insect-eating primate.

Fig. 6-5. The cebus monkey.

New World form, the night monkey, has enlarged eyes for nocturnal vision. Other New World monkeys, such as the cebus (the "organ grinder's monkey") (Fig. 6-5), the large gangling spider monkey, and the huge-throated, loud-mouthed howler monkey, have vegetarian diets: Some live chiefly on leaves, others eat fruits as well. Some New World primates (including the cebus, the spider, and howler monkeys) can grasp with the tail. The tail actually has skin-ridge patterns on the tip (like man's "fingerprints") that help it hold firmly. Such patterns in the skin of the fingers, toes, palms, and soles are found throughout the Anthropoidea.

Old World Monkeys. The Old World Monkeys are usually considered as a superfamily or a family which is divided into two subfamilies. One of these consists of the various leaf-eating monkeys of Africa and Asia. These colorful varieties are seldom seen in the zoos of the United States because in general they do not adapt well to captivity. They have large stomachs which enable them to digest bulky leaf foods. On the average, the jaws that relate to this diet are less jutting than in monkeys with a more varied diet, but in bones and, presumably, muscles of the limbs, tail, and back, the leaf monkeys do not differ much from the other Old World monkeys.

Old World monkeys also include the macaques, the monkeys most widely used in laboratory tests because, like all the higher primates, their constitution and physiology are so similar to our own. They are susceptible to most human diseases and exhibit much the same symptoms as man. The development and production of vaccines against polio depended on this fact. The macaques, baboons, and others in this subfamily show several differences. For example, different species of macaques vary in size, snout, and tail. Baboons

New York Zoological Society Photo

Fig. 6-6. Gibbon, smallest of the anthropoid apes.

grow as big as wolves while other members of this subfamily are not much bigger than squirrels.

Within this category we find a wide range of diets and ways of life. Its members are arboreal (tree dwellers) and live primarily on vegetarian diets of fruits and leaves, but the largest of these monkeys, the baboons, search for food on the ground; troops of from 9 to 185 of them have been counted. Baboons eat roots, shoots, and occasionally insects or even small animals. The limbs of baboons are adapted for four-footed movement.

The Gibbon. Man is in many ways more similar to the anthropoid apes than to the monkeys; therefore, man and apes are usually classed in a separate superfamily, the Hominoidea. There are four types of existing apes which share the term "Hominoidea" with man.

The smallest of the four anthropoid apes, the gibbons (Fig. 6-6), are placed in a subfamily of their own. Their native habitat is in Southeast Asia. They are the most agile trapeze artists of all the primates, although they share this skill with the great apes, the spider monkeys (Fig. 6-7), and, to some extent, schoolboys. A caged gibbon has been seen to swing from one arm and pluck a bird out of the air in midflight. They are generally vegetarian, however, although occasionally they may indulge a fancy for insects, a bird's egg, or even a bird.

The gibbon is also able to walk on his hind legs. On the ground he is ungainly because he must use his long arms like crutches or hold them over his head to keep them out of the way. On a tree limb, however, the gibbon can run like a tightrope walker, using his arms instead of a pole or parasol. His *bipedal* or two-footed movement is obviously quite different from man's: He is unable to extend his legs and must keep them bent. Only man can goose-step.

The Orangutan. The other Asiatic ape is the red-haired orangutan of Sumatra and Borneo. He also is a tree-top dweller who is adept at swinging by his arms. The orangutan's

New York Zoological Society Photo

Fig. 6-7.   The spider monkey easily grasps with its tail.

diet is vegetarian and includes wild fruits. Studies of the blood serum of the orangutan indicate that he is quite different in this respect from the African great apes; and probably his line of descent has long been separate from our own.

The Gorilla. There are two African great apes, the gorilla and the chimpanzee. Anatomically they are more similar to each other and, in some respects, to man than either is to the orangutan or the gibbon.

The gorilla, by far the largest primate, is relatively scarce. Some live in the lowlands of West-central Africa, the remainder in the mountains at the headwaters of the Congo. The differences between the two kinds of gorilla are not great, and were it not for hundreds of miles between them they would probably interbreed. There are few sizable trees in the mountains of Eastern Congo; the gorillas there travel on the ground,

New York Zoological Society Photo

Fig. 6-8. The gorilla travels on all fours, with the foot-sole down.

proceeding chiefly on all fours, with the foot sole-down. The
lowland gorilla has similar feet, perhaps a little less manlike.
The gorilla's posture is half erect even when he is standing on
all fours (Fig. 6-8). In four-footed walking the hand is used
with knuckles down. Even though the lowland gorilla lives in
the forest, the adult male is too big to swing by his arms in
the trees with the females and young. He is strong enough,
however, to hold his own on the ground with any animal that
might attack him. Gorillas will charge at a man, stop short,
and rear up. To threaten an intruder they bare their teeth
and beat their chests. They can become used to a friendly
man, however, and will treat him with tolerance and curiosity.
As far as we know, the diet of the wild gorilla is purely
vegetarian. That of the mountain gorilla is chiefly bamboo
shoots and succulent plants that grow at those altitudes. Per-

haps partly because of their great size—some weigh 600 pounds—and consequent ground living, the gorillas are in many ways the most manlike of the great apes. This need not mean, however, that man is more closely allied to the gorilla than to the chimpanzee.

The Chimpanzee. The chimpanzee is the best known of the great apes. It has a more extensive range in tropical Africa than the gorilla. Some smaller, or pygmy, chimpanzees are found south of the Congo River. Much like the gorilla, but more agile, the chimpanzee scurries about the trees, swinging by his arms, or walking on the outside of his feet, while progressing on all fours. The chimpanzee's lips are free, and it can produce a range of facial expressions by moving the fine muscles of the face. It can also make a variety of vocal sounds, but cannot really talk, although several attempts have been made to teach chimpanzees to do so.

Relationship of the Living Great Apes to Man

The great apes resemble man in the details of most bones, the brain, teeth, and other parts, and even the *blood groups.* Nevertheless, one should not underestimate those important respects in which the great apes are more specialized than man, or those in which man more closely resembles the gibbon, Old World monkeys, or more primitive primates. Some kinds of monkeys and some individual great apes have callous-like skin on their bottoms which may be an adaptation to sleeping seated. Man and some types of monkey lack this special area of the skin, and we presume that the human line of evolution probably separated before this and similar special features arose in those animals which have them.

It is illogical to believe that man has descended from any living type of great ape. All other primates have much shorter generations than man (chimpanzee females start to bear young at about the age of eight), which means that they have gone through even more generations and hence have had more opportunities for evolutionary change in the time since we shared common ancestors many millenia ago. While man was developing into a two-legged animal, the anthropoids were perfecting their specialties, notably the mechanism for arm swinging.

Recently Dr. Morris Goodman compared proteins of various primates with those of man. If proteins are injected into a rabbit the animal responds by forming substances in his blood serum that are called *antibodies*. Henceforth, whenever the antibodies are brought together with the same protein, they combine. In this way, for instance, a person who has been injected with polio virus proteins has antibodies which combine with and destroy live polio virus if he is exposed to the disease. Likewise antibodies can combine with proteins which resemble the original protein only in respect to part of the molecule, and it is possible to measure the degree of similarity by the amount of antibody which combines.

Dr. Goodman has prepared animal serums with antibodies which "recognize" certain kinds of protein and which measure the similarities of primates in respect to them. In this way he has been able to show that the gorilla, chimpanzee, and man are similar in respect to some serum proteins. The orangutan and the gibbon differ somewhat from the other apes and man and also from each other. The Old World monkeys come next and then the New World monkeys. The Madagascar lemurs form one distinct group by these tests, the African and Asian lorises another, and the tree shrews a third with blood proteins more distinct from those of man than are those of any other primates, but yet in some respects more similar to man's than those of representatives of other orders of mammal such as elephants and rats.

Primate Behavior

To the anthropologist the behavior in the wild of non-human primates is one of the most interesting aspects of the study of these animals. Since behavior is a subject about which little can be learned directly from fossil man, studies of other primates are a principal source of information bearing on this important aspect of the life of man's ancestors during the times before the development of human culture.

Social life is well developed in free-living monkeys and apes. Gibbons have family-sized groups with an adult male, an adult female and usually one infant and about three juveniles. Chimpanzees travel in groups of four to fourteen animals and gorillas have been counted in groups of two to thirty, always including one older male. Monkeys have still larger numbers in the group and small territories. These animals use gestures and make noises that serve to excite other members of the group to specific activities: Sexual activity, movement to a new group of trees, or an aggressive stance in relations with other animals in the region. Primates tend to position themselves in the group according to such criteria as age, sex, and social standing—if we may extend the term social standing to include degree of dominance gained by fighting, play fighting, and similar social interactions.

Culture, a Human Phenomenon

One of the chief contributions of anthropology to thought is the development of the concept of culture. This word suggests the gathering of experience by man from generation to generation mainly through the use of speech—which is, of course, the use of sounds as symbols of things and ideas. All men, even the most primitive, possess language and live in a way that is primarily learned from their forebears. No other animals do this to the same extent as man. Therefore, culture is mainly a human phenomenon. Man alone has the ability to give and use meanings by uttering verbal "symbols." Some would define man as an animal possessing a culture, but this definition of man is not satisfactory to the paleontologist, who is concerned not with man's mental development in itself but with the evolving changes in body structure represented in ancient fossil bones. He would define the human genus, *Homo*, like any other genus, purely on biological grounds. Most anthropologists define man's family (the Hominidae) so as to include all the extinct culture-producing primates.

Capacity for keen vision, two-legged locomotion, fine manipulation, varied diet, consciously planned sexual activity, vocal communication, and mental association are the biological preconditions for the development of human culture.

Playfulness, another capacity important in the development of human culture, may be seen as foreshadowed in the behavior of other primates. It is doubtful that art, philosophy, and science could have developed solely as planned activities with predetermined ends. Random activities engaged in for their own sake are certainly pleasurable to the young of many other mammals. In man, and to a lesser extent in the chimpanzee, the delay of sexual maturity and the long period of childhood dependence provide extended opportunities for play. Man's capacity for "make-believe" is, in fact, a likely road to invention.

Tools of any kind are often considered a hallmark of man. What we think of as modern man evolved, however, long after the first use of tools. That is, much of the structure of *Homo sapiens* resulted from the culture already achieved by his forebears. Any intelligent type of primate capable of using vocal communication to convey an increasing array of meanings would also make many uses of social relations. It is likely that human social life evolved together with man's biological and cultural development.

7

Evolutionary Processes and Paleontological Principles

Parallelism and Convergence. In interpreting the fossil evidence, anthropologists use principles developed on other evolutionary lines with more complete fossil records. Essentially, there are two possible interpretations that paleontologists and anthropologists can use to explain the connection between two related fossil forms. When one of a pair of related fossils is later than another, it may be reasoned that (1) the later form is directly descended (that is, evolved) from the earlier or (2) both are descended from some still earlier common ancestor. With more than two forms, various combinations of these two interpretations are possible. Some paleontologists arrange the known fossil types in a chronological sequence. Others resort to the concepts of *convergence* and *parallelism* to indicate that evolutionary similarities are believed to depend on earlier common origins.

Organisms, although of different ancestry and relationships, may be alike in living habits and appearance. The similar evolutionary development in different forms is called *convergence.* More specifically, convergence refers to the development of similar characteristics in animals that differ in ancestry but who live in a similar environment. The hummingbird and the hummingmoth, for example, have converged in their flying habits as a result of their common search for nectar in flowers as a source of food (Fig. 7-1). Due to their common environment, the bird and moth developed similar habits even though their respective ancestors differed in these habits. In other

61

Fig. 7-1. Convergence of hummingbird and hummingmoth is a result of their common search for the same food source.

words, two biologically different organisms developed similar characteristics due to the natural selection (see chapter 2) of those organisms best adapted to the common environment.

The similar evolutionary development in related forms is called *parallelism*. Parallelism, however, implies a similarity in the biological make-up of the ancestral forms; convergence does not. That is, if the ancestors of two organisms were not very different, and if evolution in the descendent lines followed more or less the same course, the term "parallelism" is used. This term is usually applied to evolving organisms that were rather similar to begin with and that were related closely enough for some of the same mutations to arise in them. The cause for parallelism is the same as that for convergence. The organisms, in order to survive in similar environments, must adapt the same biological structures. Parallelism, like convergence, is a matter of adaptation under the control of natural selection.

Adaptive Radiation. The evolutionary spread and differentiation of the descendants of one type of animal is called *adaptive radiation.* Unlike parallelism and convergence, which deal with the way two types of organisms become more similar, adaptive radiation refers to the way one type of organism evolves into progressively dissimilar organisms. The descendants of these organisms evolve to take advantage of varied environments and opportunities. Rapid changes in the external environment may cause new forms of animals to develop from a *single* ancestral type.

Adaptive radiation is well exemplified by the history of the mammals. With the geological revolution that marked the end of the Mesozoic period (the age of reptiles), the great mountain systems of the world were thrown up and previous stable climates gave way to more changeable atmospheric conditions. In these circumstances the cold-blooded dinosaurs and other reptiles could not adapt to the climate and many, therefore, became extinct as the warm-blooded mammals with internal control of their body temperature evolved in many distinct lines. The rodents specialized for gnawing, the carnivores (meat-eating animals) for hunting, the hoofed animals for grazing; the primates and sloths took to the trees; the whales, seals, and sea cows became adapted for life in the oceans; and the bats took to the air. Furthermore, each of these mammalian orders in turn gave rise to sublines that acquired new modes of life to adapt to several different environments. Many of today's mammals are far different from their primitive mammal common ancestors. In addition, various of the orders and suborders of mammals have undergone further differentiation, branching or "radiating" into types adapted to different environments. Thus, in respect to diet all the chief groups of primates include species with contrasting dietary habits. Insect-eating, leaf-eating, seed-eating, and combinations of these and other diets recurred in different branches of the primates as these branches departed more and more from the original group.

Generalized and Specialized Forms. Some evolutionists have discussed the degree to which forms are capable of further change through evolution by natural selection. Those forms that preserve the capacity to evolve are called *generalized.* By this definition man is in many ways a generalized mammal. He preserves five digits on each hand and foot and is notably lacking in such specializations as horns, tusks, wings, and hoofs. Man is specialized, however, in respect to his unusual hind limbs and his capacity for rapid movement on them. Man is also specialized in the size of his brain and the complexity of his neurological functions: No other animal has developed symbolic speech, for example. It is generally agreed that the upper limb of man is generalized and that these generalized features of man's upper limb permit him to work on and with things with his hands and become a tool maker and user.

It is easier to apply the terms "generalized" and "specialized" to fossil than to living forms. After the fact one can note that the enormous antlers of the Irish elk are a "specialization" or, since they may have contributed to the extinction of this species, an "overspecialization." But looking ahead it is hard to predict what animals of today will give rise to radiating forms and which features are generalized and can give rise to diverse new forms. The five-fingered hand is called generalized because we know that it has given rise to forms as diverse as those of the sloth and the horse. The simple mammalian external ear is not generalized, but it would be if there were some animals which had evolved external ears for locomotion, touch, or the grasping of food. That is, the identification of generalized forms can be achieved only by comparison with specialized descendants.

Pedomorphism. The evolutionary status of man has been characterized not only as plastic and generalized but also as having a third more or less independent property—that of *pedomorphism,* a term meaning childlike in form. The adult man or woman displays a number of physical traits which in other animals are seen only in the young or even in the fetus (developed from the embryo but preceding birth)—such a feature is the rounded form of the forehead. The great apes, on the other hand, show more developed features which are referred to as *gerontomorphic* (in the form of old age). Racial differences exist in respect to these features: Europeans, for example, often show gerontomorphic features, whereas some Mongoloids and the South African Bushmen have more rounded foreheads, flat faces, and other supposedly "infantile" characteristics. These features do not seem to be functionally important. The aspects of pedomorphism which do seem important have to do with behavior and not with rounded foreheads. It is the *social* infancy of humans that keeps children at home and learning from their parents for many years longer than the young of other animals.

Is Evolution Reversible? A Belgian paleontologist, Louis Dollo, in 1893 developed the theory that evolution is irreversible. There are no examples of present forms that have developed independently and that are exactly like some ancient models. There are, however, examples of the re-evolution of types highly similar in some particular respects to ancient forms. For example, the extinct flying reptiles developed wings but eventually died out; the ability to fly was re-evolved independently in the birds and bats. The likelihood of a change of the natural environment in an exact reverse order is rare; hence an occasion for reversed natural selection would be just as rare. Moreover, other organisms play a large part in the adaptation of any form of life to its natural environment. In order to survive, man, for example, depends upon many other organisms such as cattle, corn, cod, bees, yeast, and pine. If a reversal were to occur in man, it might require that these organisms also be reversing so that past human environments would be recreated. Evolution is irreversible to the extent that true throwbacks to earlier forms do not occur in detail. Single steps backward and forward in repeated and reversed mutations sometimes occur in genetic experiments. That such reversals will not repeat a whole sequence is evidence for Dollo's principle. However, according to present knowledge, the following generation is almost as likely to reverse a characteristic as to carry it forward.

The Varying Tempo of Evolution. The evolution of a species tends to be asymmetrical. That is, it may be rapid at one time, slow at another. At one time it may affect the limbs, and at another it may affect the jaws. With a change in the food supply or some other alteration in the environment, running or biting ability, for example, becomes more or less important in natural selection.

This variability in the tempo of evolution of different structural parts of organisms in the same line (that is, in ancestors and descendants) makes it unwise to draw sweeping conclusions concerning the relationship of two fossil forms on the basis of isolated characteristics. Instead, it is necessary to follow the evolution of whole functional systems. Since the systems themselves evolve at different rates, one must also take into account the total form and structure of the animal. Often the wisest response to a fragmentary fossil is to suspend judgment while one searches for additional material. A few observations considered out of context can lead the unwary anthropologist far astray.

Extinction. Direct relationships between animals that are similar in some respects are often too easily assumed. Some animal forms survive—especially in out-of-the-way places—long after their ancestors have given rise to quite different descendants elsewhere. Whole populations are not likely to become totally extinct, however. Even with the overrunning of other lands by Europeans in the last three centuries, Hottentots and Hopis, Polynesians and Pygmies, still survive. Although the last pure Tasmanian, a dark, woolly-haired woman called Truganini, died in 1877, many descendants of Tasmanians mixed with Australian aborigines and Europeans do survive to this day.

In tracing relations between fossils we need not imply direct ancestry. We merely refer to the group in which the individual is classified. Arrows of relatedness on evolutionary charts should be taken to show connecting groups (that is, populations, species, or larger categories). These charts do not indicate kinship between the former owners of individual skeletons. Anthropologists have, sometime in the past, emphasized details in their fossil material that may very well represent nothing more than individual peculiarities. Members of a given group will vary, to some extent, in respect to particular bones, for example. Isolated fossils must be judged in terms of the probable degree of this variability. Of course, when only one specimen is available, the probable degree of variability can only be inferred from similar features in other groups of men or other animals.

8

Some Fossil Primates

Geological Time Scale

Animal *fossils* are any traces or remains (most frequently parts of the skeleton) of animals of past geological ages. Under forest conditions bones usually disintegrate before they fossilize. Tree-living tropical animals, such as primates, therefore leave relatively few fossils. Nevertheless, a surprisingly wide variety of primates are known from fossilized bones. All the primate fossils so far discovered belong to forms which lived during the last 70 million years or so. Indeed, all fossils of mammals belong to the same period, the Cenozoic Era, except for a very few primitive mammals which first appeared in the preceding era, the age of the dinosaurs.

Geologists divide the *Cenozoic Era* into six epochs (*Paleocene, Eocene, Oligocene, Miocene, Pliocene,* and *Pleistocene*). These names designate the periods of time during which suc-

Era	Epochs	Approximate Time Since Beginning (in millions of years)
	Paleocene	71
	Eocene	60
Cenozoic	Oligocene	40
	Miocene	30
	Pliocene	10
	Pleistocene	1

Fig. 8-1.   Time scale of Cenozoic era.

cessive layers or strata of rock were deposited. The earliest Cenozoic deposits are dated at approximately 71 million years ago by calculations on the amount of radioactive decay of certain minerals found in deposits at the bottom (hence the beginning) of the Cenozoic strata.

Rocks deposited during the following epochs of the Cenozoic Era are dated relative to each other by their position in places where they can be seen (such as on the walls of canyons) and by the changing nature of the fossils contained within them. The approximate dates of these epochs are indicated in Figure 8-1.

The last epoch of the Cenozoic, the Pleistocene, is the period of the great glaciations and extended from a million or so years ago up until the last few thousand years. All the definitely human fossils known come from deposits of the Pleistocene Epoch.

Unfortunately the date at which the Pleistocene Epoch began is not very well established. The marked cooling of the first of the four great glaciations occurred about 600,000 years ago to judge from tentative correlations between climates and the astronomical events which may have caused them. Before that, however, there was an extended period with cool climates but no major glaciations. It is called the *Villafranchian* and its duration is not really known but often arbitrarily given as about 400,000 years. It may have had a longer duration to judge from the fact that fossils of various types of animals which are ordinarily found together in deposits of Villafranchian age have been found in at least one site with an antiquity of 2,500,000 years. This date is based on the rate of decay of certain radioactive elements in the rock formations around the fossils (the potassium-argon method).

The Primates

At the very beginning of the Cenozoic Era, the primitive Primates developed several distinct varieties. Some of these seem to have had limbs specialized for jumping, others for climbing, but most are known only from teeth. The lemurs and tarsiers of today are, to some extent, foreshadowed in these first primates, but it is not possible to say with confidence exactly which of the early fossil primate types eventually gave rise to man. A considerable variety of fossil lemurs of the Pleistocene Epoch from Madagascar and a number of types on that island and in Africa and Southern Asia today, represent a group of primitive primates which evolved during the same periods as the higher primates.

Primate fossils of the Eocene Epoch (about 60 million years ago) have been found in Europe, Africa, and Asia. In a few cases the same types occurred in both hemispheres. In subsequent periods, however, primate evolution in the New World has apparently been quite separate from that in the Old. The few New World fossils of monkeys which are known could have been ancestral to modern types of American monkeys, but not to African monkeys, Asian monkeys, apes, or man.

In the Old World and beginning with the Oligocene Epoch (about 40 million years ago) a variety of fossils of higher primates are known. Among the earliest of these are three fossils from Egypt which are of types foreshadowing monkeys and apes. One of these seems rather like the gibbon and a long separate history for the gibbon is also suggested by somewhat gibbon-like fossils of the next epoch, the Miocene (about 30 million years ago), from both Europe and Africa. These fossils have relatively long arm bones and projecting teeth at the corners of the mouth (the canine teeth) much as in modern gibbons.

Proconsul. Dr. and Mrs. L. S. B. Leakey, whose names will recur because they discovered several of the primate fossils which bear most directly on human evolution, extracted a nearly intact skull and other parts of the skeleton of a primate called Proconsul. These come from the same Miocene deposits in East Africa which yield gibbon-like fossils. Proconsul, however, is not very specialized in the direction of modern arm-swinging apes. He is, in the views of some, a primitive (monkey-like) ape of the type one might expect in a common ancestor of both man and the modern African great apes, the gorilla and the chimpanzee.

Oreopithecus. Between the Miocene Proconsul and the Early Pleistocene South African man apes there was a time interval of over ten million years. Some fossils discovered in coal mines of Tuscany in Italy help to fill this gap in our knowledge. Most of the earlier reports concerning these so-called Oreopithecus specimens were written by scholars who never saw the specimens but relied on casts or previous descriptions. New explorations of the lignite coal fields of Tuscany reveal Oreopithecus deposits together with fossils of Early Pliocene date (about 10 million years ago). Examination of all the Oreopithecus material now available shows several generalized hominid (of man's own family) features of the teeth and jaws, such as small canine teeth and short face, a resemblance which, some students believe, associates Oreopithecus more closely with man than with the great apes or the monkeys. Some features of the skull, jaws, and fragments of limb bones lead to the same conclusion, although the limb bones are generalized and in other ways resemble those of monkeys rather than those of apes or man. The hand may have been long, a feature shared with arm-swinging apes. The vertebrae at the base of the spinal column are so large and strong, it is said, as not to exclude the possibility that Oreopithecus could walk upright. If this description is confirmed by further studies and additional finds of fossils, Oreopithecus may represent our first glimpse of a member of the human family. On the other hand, in classifying Oreopithecus, some authorities consider it too monkey-like to be an actual ancestor of man. They believe that Oreopithecus and one of the fossils from Fayum, Egypt are part of an evolutionary line which is now extinct. It is more plausible, they say, that man's ancestors were evolving elsewhere at that time. Perhaps these first members of the human family are represented by two bits of upper jaw and a lower tooth, also of early Pliocene age, which Leakey has found in East Africa.

The Discovery of Australopithecus

A series of fossils have been found in Africa, mostly in limestone deposits formed by the collapse and filling up of caves. In 1924 a South African quarryman working near a place called Taungs blasted out a small fossilized skull. He sent it to the anatomist at a South African medical school, Professor Raymond Dart. Dart noted a number of resemblances to human skulls that are not shared by chimpanzees or gorillas. Dart called the species *Australopithecus africanus*, which means "southern ape from Africa" and has nothing to do with Australia.

Dr. Robert Broom, who had been studying fossils of mammal-like reptiles, went to see the skull. He became convinced of its importance and searched for more evidence. In the years which followed, Broom, Dart, the Leakeys, and others have found similar specimens in six other places in Africa, from the extreme south to the Sahara Desert.

In one instance, two of Dart's students took Broom to a lime quarry where the foreman knew something about their search for fossils. The foreman sold Broom a specimen which he in turn had purchased from a young school boy. Broom went to see the boy, Gert Terblanche, who was out playing. The boy still had in his pocket four fossil teeth. He also took Broom to a place where he had hidden a very fine jaw with some beautiful teeth.

More recently, on July 17, 1959 to be exact, and far to the north in a dry ravine called Olduvai Gorge, Dr. and Mrs. Leakey discovered a skull imbedded in the side of the cliff. Fortunately, the skull was in its original place in the cliff and it has been possible to show that it is at the same level as some crude stone tools and flakes—presumably used by this creature. The deposit also contained some bones of small ani-

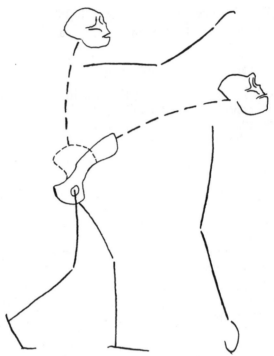

Drawn by Stanley Washburn

Fig. 8-2.   Posture of great ape and Australopithecus.

mals—probably the remains of meals. Still other specimens have been found at a deeper level at Olduvai.

Skulls and Jaws of Australopithecus. The original specimen of Australopithecus was that of a young individual. Since in the young of chimpanzees, as well as of man, the part of the skull which contains the brain grows much faster during infancy than do the jaws, the rather human appearance, in this respect, of the young of chimpanzees and Australopithecus should not deceive one. But even the full-grown Australopithecus skulls have some surprisingly human aspects. The brain case itself is not large: The brain must have weighed about a pound, which is little if any bigger than those of living apes and only a third to a half the size of that of most normal men.

The jaws are also powerful and ape-like, some of the specimens being of truly enormous proportions. The strength for chewing with these big jaws is represented by the markings on the skulls where the muscles attached. In some of the specimens crests of bone of the same general type as those found in adult male gorillas and chimpanzees (and big dogs, for that matter) have grown out to give attachment to the forceful muscles with which Australopithecus ate his presumably raw meals. The back teeth are also very large, but the front teeth are comparatively small. The corner teeth, which are long and interlocking and used for self-defense by monkeys and apes, are so reduced in Australopithecus as to imply that he used his hands and presumably held weapons when he needed to defend himself or hunt for his meals.

Gait of Australopithecus. The hip bones of man and apes are very different, and here Australopithecus shows his closest resemblance to man. The upper part (ilium) is spread out, as in modern man. The elongation of this part, which is typical of the ape, does not occur in Australopithecus (Fig. 8-2). One hip bone in particular shows some ape-like features in the lower part (ischium) that suggest that Australopithecus ran with his knees bent. The few pieces of fossil bones of the Australopithecus lower limb belong to an animal intermediate in size between the chimpanzee and man, but with an essentially human manner of getting about. The segments of the Australopithecus backbone are of human type. To judge from the position of the hole for the spinal cord and the markings left by the muscles which held the head in place, the head apparently attached on top of the neck rather than being thrust forward as in non-human primates. Insofar as the skeletal anatomy can indicate, Australopithecus must have had a more upright stance than is seen in any of the living apes.

Recently, deliberately worked stone tools have been found

Courtesy of John T. Robinson
and Robert Broom

Fig. 8-3.   Australopithecus skull of the larger variety.

in some of the deposits. Some of these are primitive versions of the so-called *Chelles-Acheul Industry* which is associated with more advanced individuals (see below). In other places they are of earlier "pebble-tool" type. Bone and wooden objects may also have been used. The existence of presumably Australopithecus tools agrees with the idea that once man-like animals had achieved upright stance, they could conveniently hold tools and weapons while running or walking. Both developments must have gone on together and represent the beginning of distinctively human evolution.

One should not minimize, however, the fact that specimens of Australopithecus are quite varied. Two or more main types occur (Figs. 8-3 and 8-4). The bones of one of these are massive. A more human trend is seen especially in one of the smaller specimens of jaw bone. The time span occupied by creatures of this general type may also have been considerable. All the specimens are thought to belong to the early part of the Pleistocene Epoch, that is, to the Villafranchian period which preceded the ice ages of North Europe and North America. In Africa there were no ice ages, but a series of dry and rainy periods. The shapes of grains of sand in the Australopithecus deposits seem to establish that these were formed during more than one climatic period since in only some cases was the sand from a desert, blown into the limestone caves by the wind during one of the dry periods. An antiquity of 1,750,000 years has been claimed for one specimen on the basis of potassium-argon tests. Much later dates seem probable for most, if not all, of the specimens. In any case, one can never definitely exclude the possibility that more advanced types of "ape-men" were developing elsewhere while a more primitive form survived for a while and then became extinct. If the earliest Australopithecus specimens lived long ago, they may well be direct ancestors. But even if they are

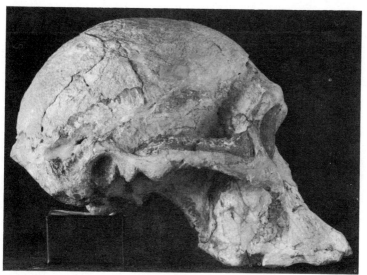

Courtesy of John T. Robinson and Robert Broom

Fig. 8-4.   Australopithecus skull of the smaller variety.

merely an extinct, separate branch, they can tell us much about the appearance of human ancestors. Australopithecus suggests that upright stance and use of hand tools in all probability preceded the evolution of a large brain and the keeping of fires.

9

Fossil Man

Homo erectus (Pithecanthropus). As we have seen, Australopithecus bridges the gap between man and earlier extinct fossil primates. But Australopithecus is a small-brained creature, for all of his presumed ability to get about on two feet and wield weapons in his hands. The step from such a creature to modern man does not involve missing links, however, because for many years examples of fossil men with varying degrees of brain development have been turning up in deposits of the Pleistocene Epoch in various parts of the Old World.

In 1891 and 1892, during a deliberate search on the island of Java for a "missing link" between the apes and man, a Dutch physician, Eugene Dubois, discovered a thigh bone and the top part of the skull of a man of this stage. He gave it the name *Pithecanthropus erectus,* erect ape-man, because the thigh bone is entirely like that of modern erect humans whereas the skull is low and has a thick brutish-appearing bar of bone (the *supraorbital torus*) over both eye sockets. It is somewhat similar in this respect to the gorilla. More recently, additional specimens have been found in Java. The brain-containing cavities of these skulls are intermediate in size between those of modern men on the one hand and those of the great apes and Australopithecus on the other. The jaws are very large and lack a protruding chin (Fig. 9-1). Despite these differences some scholars put these fossils in man's own group, the genus *Homo,* and call them *Homo erectus,* upright man. The distinctly human features include the presence of a *mastoid process* (the bony prominence of the skull behind the ear lobe in man), the general form of the jaws, the details of

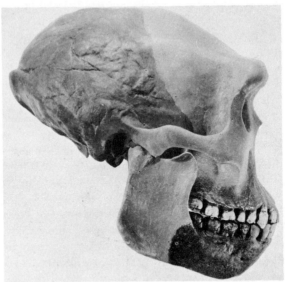

Fig. 9-1.   Reconstruction of skull of Java Man.

the surface patterns of the teeth, and, as mentioned earlier, the human limb bones.

Although, presumably, tools were used, they have not been found. The deposits in Java from which these fossils came were not those of filled caves, but riverbanks. Therefore, it is hardly surprising that if there were stone tools they might well have been separated from the bones and lost.

Peking Man.   In any case, a similar type of fossil has been excavated in some quantity from a cave deposit near Peking, China. Peking Man, as this form is called, was found with his crude stone tools and the evidence of fires which probably were intentionally maintained for warmth and cooking. The fossils from the cave near Peking have slightly larger brain cavities than the ones from Java. The Peking fossils have a few other differences such as front teeth which are hollow behind (shovel-shaped). Today this shape of tooth is most frequently seen in Eastern Asiatic people. Nevertheless, except for a few anthropologists who believe that such minor distinctions may persist for a long time in a particular racial subgroup, most students of the matter believe that the Javanese and Chinese fossils are closely related to each other and very distinct from any group of modern men.

Homo erectus is said to date from the Early and Middle Pleistocene. In Java at least two time periods seem to have been spanned by this form and the earlier one may overlap with the latest period during which Australopithecus is known to have been alive in Africa. The later one has been dated at about 500,000 years ago by the potassium-argon method. Peking Man was not much later on the scene and, largely on the basis of the other fossils found with him, is also ascribed to the Middle Pleistocene.

Ronald Singer

Fig. 9-2.   Four hand-axes discovered in Africa.

Other Middle Pleistocene Fossil Men. In Europe, Africa, and Western Asia, Middle Pleistocene deposits have yielded a type of human stone tool in which a stone has been sharpened by knocking big chips off both sides. This instrument is sometimes called a hand-axe although we have no certainty that it was used in the way the term suggests (Fig. 9-2). The general term for these stone tools is the *Chelles-Acheul Industry* after the places in France where two types of hand axe were first found. Such hand axes are numerous in the open Middle Pleistocene terraces of the rivers of Europe and elsewhere, but fossil remains of their users have been scarce. In Morocco and Algeria, Chelles-Acheul tools have turned up together with three lower jaw bones of their users. These jaws are very similar to those of Peking Man. Furthermore, at Olduvai, but in a deposit about 360,000 years old, much later than the ones where the specimens of Australopithecus type were found, the Leakeys also discovered a skull together with Chelles hand axes. This skull is very similar to those of Java and China, although it is larger and has a supraorbital torus which is, if anything, even more prominent. It clearly belongs with *Homo erectus* in the inclusive sense in which the term is here being used.

Some other fragmentary specimens from Java, East Africa, and South Africa are thought by some scholars to be roughly at the level of Australopithecus, by others to be more comparable to *Homo erectus*. Since some of these individuals were contemporaneous (lived at the same time) with Australopithecus in Africa while others were contemporaneous with *Homo erectus* in Java, they may bridge the gap. Alternatively they may indicate that before Australopithecus became extinct there were already more human types about. According to this view, Australopithecus was too late to be in the line of human ancestry. Other, more advanced forms were contemporaneous, and it was the more human forms that made the first tools, which they may have used to hunt and kill their distant cousin, Australopithecus.

The Neandertaloids.   Human fossils with characteristics intermediate between *Homo erectus* and our own species (*Homo sapiens,* which means "wise man") are found in many parts of the world (but not the Americas). They also vary in many details and may not all have equal significance for the evolution of our species. Nevertheless, besides occupying the same quarter million or so years (up to about 50,000 years ago), they also have some common features: Brains of the same range of sizes as our own, long rugged skulls with ridges of bone both above the eye sockets and also in back where the neck muscles attach, low foreheads, powerful jaws with large teeth but little or no chin, and, in the rest of the body, bones of essentially modern human type.

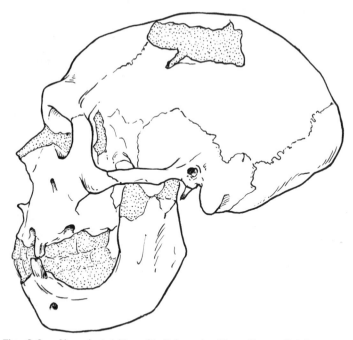

Fig. 9-3.   Neandertal Man. Skull from La Chapelle-aux-Saints.

In Europe, North Africa, and Western Asia there developed a surprisingly consistent form which we call *Neandertal Man*. The most typical examples come from cave deposits of the last Interglacial stage or the first phase of the Last Glaciation about 100,000 years ago. They are found together with special types of stone tools (called *Mousterian*) which include some which look as if they were used for scraping skins. Fur clothing was, therefore, probably worn, and there is little reason to believe that these men were themselves necessarily hairy. There are fireplaces in the caves and the dead were buried rather than merely left where they died. The skull was set forward on the spine (Fig. 9-3) but there is no good reason to suppose this man stooped with his knees sharply bent as he has so often been pictured.

Fossils of somewhat similar forms extend further back in time and to a wider variety of places. In Europe a skull from Steinheim was found together with bones of warm-climate animals of interglacial types and is thought to date back to the great middle interglacial period of the Pleistocene Epoch. The skull is small and the region about the ear is of more modern type than in the later Neandertals.

In the Near East there are quite typical Neandertal specimens, such as those from the Shanidar Valley in Northern Iraq, with long faces and small mastoid processes behind the ear. Other, less typical specimens have been discovered at Mount Carmel in Palestine. These are intermediate in some respects between Neandertal Man of Western Europe and modern man; some resemble one the more, some the other. The supraorbital ridges, although large, are divided in the middle, and in some specimens the back of the skull is rounded and the face is more delicate with a definite chin as in modern man. But, although more evolved in some details, these specimens are early in date: the end of the Last Interglacial or the beginning of the Last Glacial period.

Since more advanced specimens apparently preceded the typical Neandertal Man, some anthropologists believe that, at

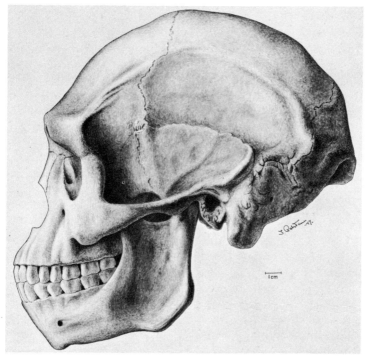

American Museum of
Natural History

Fig. 9-4.   Solo Man skull reconstruction.

one time, there were two different grades of men, perhaps occasionally mating with each other but, in general, distinct.
The Neandertal type, they suggest, was well adapted to the
cold of the ice ages but soon became extinct when this advantage no longer served him. There is little if any reason to support this view, however.

Africa and the Far East were also inhabited at this time.
Quite recently a fossil has been found at Mapa in South China
which, to judge from a preliminary description and illustra-
tions, is similar to the European and Western Asiatic Neandertals. The skull is low and the ridges above the round

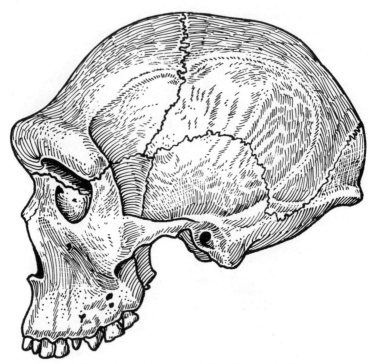

Fig. 9-5. Skull of Rhodesian Man (after Montagu). Note the supra-orbital torus.

Neandertal-like orbits form a bony ridge intermediate but more like that of Neandertal than like that of Solo Man (see below). This skull was found together with fossil animal types of the end of the Middle or beginning of the Late Pleistocene. It appears to be clearly Neandertaloid although some Chinese scholars who have examined it put it in a more primitive category.

Solo Man. Besides specimens of *Homo erectus* and two large jaws which may possibly belong to Australopithecus, if that term is used very inclusively, Java is the source of eleven skulls and two leg bones discovered along the banks of the

Solo River in a terrace which has been dated to the Late Pleistocene. These skulls have room for only relatively small brains. They have marked ridges above the orbits that slope straight back into the forehead whereas, in the other fossil skulls described, the forehead is separated by a hollow area and, no matter how low, it has a distinct curve. The back of the skull is also thickened and the part at the base, which is buried in the neck during life, also shows distinctions from Neandertal Man and from man today (Fig. 9-4). Nevertheless, Solo Man has been described as Neandertaloid (like Neandertal Man) although some features line it up more closely with *Homo erectus*. The leg bones are essentially of modern type but so, for that matter, are the leg bones of all fossil men.

Rhodesian Man. The term Neandertaloid has also been loosely extended to cover the human remains blasted from a quarry at Broken Hill, Rhodesia in 1921. Rhodesian Man, as

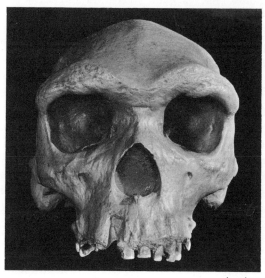

*American Museum of
Natural History*

Fig. 9-6.   Front view of cast of skull of Rhodesian Man.

he is called, has a face which is flat but protruding. The supra-orbital torus extends to the outer edge of the orbits and is comparable in size to that of a gorilla (Figs. 9-5 and 9-6). The area for attachment of neck muscles is similar to that of Solo Man, and the skull of Rhodesian Man resembles those of Solo Man rather more closely than the nearer North African and Near Eastern Neandertals. In any case, it is considered to be at a Neandertaloid developmental level. The robust jaw contains diseased teeth. Dental decay, a bane of civilization, is rare in fossil man but besides Rhodesian Man, several Australopithecus teeth are affected and the disease occurs occasionally in living non-human primates.

A few years ago at a place near Saldanha Bay, about 90 miles from the southernmost tip of Africa, a large number of fossil bones (about 20 per cent of them of extinct forms) were found together with many stone tools, including hand axe types. Besides teeth of giant wart hogs and horns of buffaloes with a spread of a dozen feet, the fossils include a human skull cap almost identical to that part in Rhodesian Man.

The date of this deposit has been estimated as of the order of 100,000 to 200,000 years ago, but it is well to bear in mind that the objects were found on the surface where they had been left behind as the wind blew the covering grains of sand away. Not all the forms need have been alive at the same time. Among the remains there was also a piece of human jaw bone which presumably belonged to the same type of individual as the skull cap. The jaw bone fragment is said to be particularly reminiscent of a large fossil jaw found near Heidelberg, Germany, in 1907, which is of considerable interest since it is supposed to be from the first interglacial or second glacial period, nearly half a million years ago.

The Origin of Modern Man

In implying a transition in type (although not necessarily actual ancestral relationships) from Australopithecus to *Homo erectus* to the Neandertaloids to modern man, it has been necessary to group the individual fossils into these major grades. This is justifiable only if one believes that the considerable differences between the fossils which are grouped together represent individual variability. Mankind today is variable and so are some species of non-human primates. In this view, the human evolutionary picture is of a succession of variable forms descending from each other by a netlike web from the somewhat different types of the preceding grade. The picture loses force to the extent that the later members of any grade are less like ourselves than some earlier members. Thus, the big-jawed and least human of the two Australopithecus types is apparently later than some specimens of the more generalized type. And in the case of the

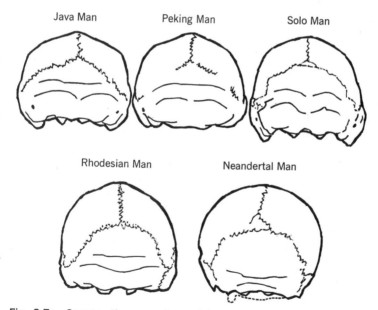

Fig. 9-7. Comparative rear views of fossil men (after Weidenreich). Note the development of the brain case and shape of the skulls.

Neandertaloids, the classic Neandertal specimens of Western Europe and Asia are primitive but relatively recent. These examples of continuation of more primitive forms in some places while more modern types were evolving elsewhere merely indicate that the stream of human evolution has not been a smooth one. Instead, there have been eddies of survival of earlier types for a while here or there.

Some critics go further, however, and claim that modern forms of man evolved a very long time ago, before many of the specimens which we have discussed. The evidence on which this claim is based consists primarily of a few fossils which are said to be early specimens of *Homo sapiens*, our own kind of man. The two finds most frequently cited in this connection are from Swanscombe, England, and Fontéchevade, France.

At Swanscombe, an amateur archeologist found several pieces of the side and back of a skull in a deposit left by the Thames River when it was 100 feet higher, probably during the long Second Interglacial period to judge by animal fossils found at the level. Furthermore, the skull fragments show the same degree of fossilization as these other bones. The tools, too, include Acheul hand axes which also are earlier than the Mousterian types used by Neandertal Man. It is true that there is little to distinguish the skull fragments from the same parts of modern man and that the back of the skull is more rounded than in Neandertal Man. On the other hand, however, the general form of the skull resembles Rhodesian Man and a bony ridge behind the ear is similar to this feature in Neandertal skulls and suggests that the missing mastoid process may have been of Neandertal type. Furthermore, the skull is of a young individual, perhaps only 20 years old, and a Neandertal youth of this age would not be expected to differ much from modern man in respect to the parts of the skull known from Swanscombe.

The Fontéchevade specimens were found on what had been the floor of a cave. This floor was covered by, and hence earlier than, a deposit containing Mousterian types of stone tools. The animal fossils found with the two human skull fragments are of forms associated with the warm to temperate climate of the Last Interglacial period. The first specimen shows a weak development of the supraorbital ridges. The second specimen is of somewhat the same shape as the corresponding part of a young Neandertal skull, but apparently did not have Neandertal Man's type of protruding supraorbital ridges. Although there is little to distinguish these specimens from modern man, there is also little to mark them off from Neandertaloid types.

Other examples of allegedly early specimens of modern type have been shown either to be of doubtful antiquity or are too fragmentary to tell us much. One, the Piltdown Man, was a fraud. Another, a jaw from Kanam in East Africa, is believed

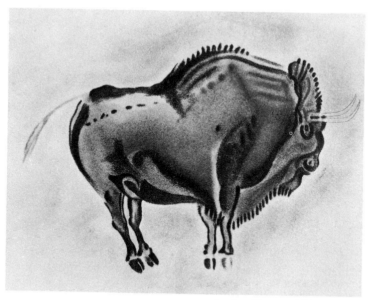

American Museum of Natural History

Fig. 9-8.   Upper Paleolithic cave painting of a bison.

by some not to be as ancient as was claimed. In any case, a cancerous growth near the chin has distorted this part of the specimen.

Modern man was first definitely on the scene only when the last great glaciation was melting and shrinking northward across Europe. The great woolly mammoth became extinct and there was an increase of the herds of wild cattle, horses, and reindeer. The men of these times painted the animals on the walls of their cave homes (Fig. 9-8). Many skeletons of the people of this period, the Upper Paleolithic, have been found. These last men of the Old Stone Age were entirely of our own sort, *Homo sapiens*. In fact, they are generally considered to belong to the same race as contemporary Europeans.

Some anthropologists have thought that they saw racial differences between some of the Upper Paleolithic men of Europe. There is little to be said for this view. There certainly are individual differences but there are also many features common to these men. The skulls are generally long and narrow, the jaws powerful, and the faces short but robust. The effort to match specimens of the period with modern racial groups is doomed to failure. There are many intervening generations of further evolution and intermingling. Although the subsequent change has been minor compared with the whole span of primate evolution, it does prevent any specific identification of the ancestors of particular peoples of today.

In other parts of the world, also, the earliest specimens of *Homo sapiens* are often pointed out as ancestors of today's populations. In Africa the fossils are described as ancestral Bushmen, Hottentots, or Negroes; in China as Mongoloids, and so on. In fact, however, these early specimens of *Homo sapiens* probably differed less from each other than does man today. The muscle markings and general appearance of bones of men from Late Pleistocene deposits at Florisbad in Africa, Hotu in Iran, Peking and Tzu-yang in China, and many other places are comparable to what we know of the men of that period from Europe, North Africa, and the Near East.

Early Man In America

The same similarities to European Upper Paleolithic features which are found during the same period in Africa and Asia may be seen in the most ancient human skulls from the Americas. Although there is some doubt about the exact antiquity of such skulls as those of Minnesota Man from the United States, Tepexpan Man from Mexico, and Punin Man from Ecuador, the stone tools of the first human beings in the New World are better known and dated. This has been done by the carbon-14 method. Living things, such as trees, absorb a certain constant amount of radioactive carbon-14 from the air. The date when remains of a tree stump were part of a living tree can therefore be determined by the amount of radioactive decay that has taken place. The last land bridge from Asia to America blocked the shallow channel between Alaska and Siberia from about 25,000 years ago until about 10,000 or 11,000 years ago. Man discovered America during that period if not earlier. Some of the known American skeletal remains may, therefore, pertain to the same period as the Upper Paleolithic in the Old World. Although human stone tools excavated in the United States have been shown by the carbon-14 method to be several times as old, the earliest definite date we have for a human skeleton in the New World may not be more than 7000 years ago. This is the minimum carbon-14 date for a *Homo sapiens* skeleton of American Indian characteristics, discovered at Midland, Texas, beneath a stratum containing an American type of Upper Paleolithic tool. In general, the American skulls with the best claims to considerable antiquity are somewhat but not markedly "Amerindian," as anthropologists sometimes call the American Indians. The early skulls also suggest the Australian or even the European with big brow ridges and prominent jaws. Probably these are merely the common features of early *Homo sapiens* wherever he is found.

10

Measurement of Man

The technique of measuring differences in human form is called *anthropometry*. This technique is used for the purpose of understanding relationships between various groups of people and as an aid in determining their origins. Over one hundred years ago, Dr. Anders Retzius, a Swede, demonstrated that the ratio of maximum length to maximum breadth of the skull varies from place to place and that the *cephalic index*, as he called it, can be used as a basis for racial classification. Retzius also considered the *degree of prognathism* (the extent to which the jaw protrudes) in his racial classification. Various points on the skull can be used for measurements.

In 1879, anatomists interested in anthropology, meeting at a convention in Frankfurt, Germany, agreed upon a standard position for holding the skull. The so-called "Frankfurt horizontal" or "eye-ear plane" (Fig. 10-1) consists of a plane through the top of both ear holes and the lowest point on the lower margin of the orbits. By adding a vertical plane that bisects the skull (the median plane) and a third plane at right angles to both of these, through the ear holes, any point on the skull can be located by noting the shortest distance from each of these three planes. If enough measurements are made by means of these coordinates, one can describe a skull accurately enough for someone else to draw it.

The techniques of statistical analysis have been applied to the study of human groups with much success. Statistical studies of measurements of man led to a decreased emphasis on types and an increased awareness of the overlapping range

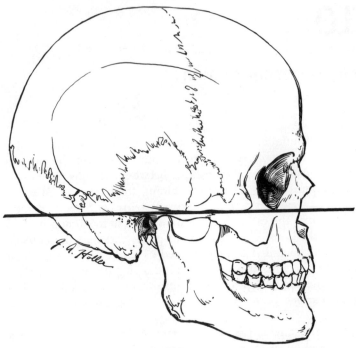

Fig. 10-1. Eye-ear plane through the top of both ear holes and lower margin of the orbits.

of possible shapes of body, head, and face between each people and its neighbors.

Most important among the measurements of the various peoples of the world have been stature, trunk height, limb lengths, and length, breadth, and height of the head, face, nose, and eye orbits. On the average, people differ from region to region in these measurements. It soon became clear that these differences in average dimensions permit valid generalizations: In many cases the differences between populations are greater than one would expect to find in two random samples drawn from the same lot. It was generally assumed, therefore, that these "real" differences were racial—

that is, they provided evidence of different genetic origins. The technique of adding measurement to measurement was designed to increase the precision of the description. Such descriptions of peoples became quite precise. Anthropologists had begun to wonder whether the characteristics described were entirely hereditary in origin and how much they could tell us about race.

The Measurement of Growth. As noted earlier, the techniques of anthropometry were developed at a time when it was believed that they could be used to solve the problems of race. While this hope has waned, new uses of the techniques have emerged. When anthropologists wished to compare the measurements of two groups of adults, the question soon arose: At what age do people reach their adult dimensions? The solution was sought by arranging the statures by age groups and seeing at what age there were no longer increases in stature. It was noted that this age occurred later in men than in women and later during periods of starvation than during periods of plenty. The anthropologist was now fully engaged in study of the questions of physiological adolescence and the growth process.

When statures of individuals are arranged by age, it is seen that there are certain periods of very rapid growth and certain periods of slower progress. The first spurt normally follows the first week of life and continues at a gradually decreased rate for the first four years or so. Growth then continues at a slower pace but starts to go ahead faster again in the period before sexual maturity (puberty). During the interval, girls, who on the average are smaller at birth than boys, briefly exceed the boys in average height. In various groups which have been studied, this period usually occurs from the age of about 9 to that of about 12. The growth of girls slows down after puberty, and their stature reaches stability several years later, while boys reach puberty later and continue to grow at least into their twenties.

The above description is very general. There are considerable differences that depend on race and environment, and, furthermore, there are marked individual differences.

The first recorded instance of a systematic attempt to follow the growth of an individual was undertaken between April 11, 1759, and January 30, 1777. During this period, Philibert Gueneau de Montbeillard, a French country gentleman, periodically measured his son's height. On the basis of these data his friend, the celebrated French naturalist Georges Louis Leclerc de Buffon, noted that growth is greater in summer than in winter. Buffon also was the first to state that height tends to decrease during the day and increase after a night's rest.

Information of this kind and also conclusions concerning individual differences in the growth process can be derived only from remeasuring the same individuals. Such a growth study is called *longitudinal* (Fig. 10-2), while surveys employing only one examination of each individual are called *cross-sectional.*

T. Wingate Todd, professor of anatomy at Western Reserve University, noted that the ages at which various bones are formed and at which the parts of a bone fuse with each other are closely related to the growth process, and he introduced the concept of "physiological age" as a measure of growth progress. Predictions of adult stature based on the degree of bone formation (ossification) already achieved are more reliable than those based on achieved size alone.

Growth and Health. Endocrinal, nutritional, and other diseases of childhood usually affect the rate of growth; hence, individual progress in growth in weight or in the ratio of stature to weight serves as an index of health. Several different schemes have been devised whereby a physician or teacher can look for variations in the growth pattern that may reflect ill health. One of these methods is that of Dr. N. C. Wetzel, a Cleveland pediatrician, who has produced a graph on which weight is plotted on the vertical axis and height on the horizontal. As a child grows in both dimensions the plotted dots

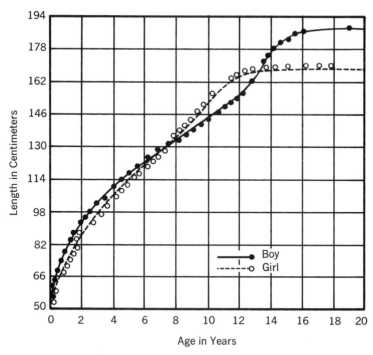

Courtesy of Jean Deming

Fig. 10-2. Growth charts of body length measurements in an individual boy and girl. This type of study is longitudinal.

angle upward toward the right. The graph has a series of diagonal lines drawn toward the upper right, and Wetzel calls the spaces between these lines "channels." The scales are so designed that a normally healthy child will tend to stay in the same channel. Deviations from channelwise growth or lack of a normal amount of growth within the channel are suggestive of ill health. Other types of chart serve the same purpose. All suffer, however, from the difficulty that healthy growth varies from race to race and person to person, and that "normal" is impossible to define satisfactorily. Most anthropologists define normal in statistical terms—that is, "like most other children."

Wetzel is less specific about how he uses anthropometric data in establishing his norms: For him they have clinical as well as statistical meaning.

Differential Growth. The type of chart mentioned in the previous section can ultimately give no information except about height and weight. These are compound measurements that encompass the joint effects of many factors and are, therefore, excellent measures of general size. However, for the purpose of understanding growth and gathering information about the growing individual's state of health, it is important to measure growth of the body segments. Once this need was recognized, anthropologists were ready with techniques for measuring just such body segments. It was soon apparent that different parts of the body grow at different rates at different times. For example, by the time of birth, the human head has come to dominate the little body, but during the postnatal period the body and then the limbs tend to spurt ahead to produce adult proportions. Growth is thus asymmetrical in the same way that evolution is asymmetrical. In human development the head grows rapidly, then the limbs and trunk, and the ears and nose continue to grow throughout life; in human evolution the hind limbs apparently evolved rapidly before the main expansion of the brain and skull, and some changes in details of the external nose and ears are probably recent. Although there is no simple alternation of "spring up" and "spread out" during growth, as was once believed, various lengths and breadths grow fastest at different times.

The tissues of the body as well as the segments show different growth patterns. Various glands develop early in childhood and actually regress considerably in adulthood. The brain and other nervous tissues also develop early, and their growth slows down in early childhood. The gonads (ovaries and testes), on the other hand, and the secondary sexual tissues, such as breasts, develop very little at first but suddenly spurt ahead at puberty. Most other body tissues show an intermediate type of growth that reflects general growth: They show the infantile and pubescent spurts and more moderate growth rates between these times. A growth curve of muscle or bone is similar to one of stature or weight.

Body Fat.   Growth in fat has come to have special interest because statisticians working for life insurance companies have cited evidence that fat persons, especially fat men, have a shorter expectation of life than average or lean persons. Fat people seem especially subject to certain heart and kidney ailments. Only recently, anthropologists have begun to test and use a variety of methods of measuring body fat: Subcutaneous fat (fat under the skin) can be determined by picking up a double fold of skin and underlying tissue and applying a measuring instrument (caliper) that exerts a known pressure; subcutaneous fat can also be measured on X rays. Total body fat can be estimated from specific gravity, which is determined by dunking the person and measuring the volume or the weight of water displaced.

Total body fat can be roughly measured by body weight or by some index using height and weight. So measured, the amount of fat has long been known to depend on the amount of food eaten. The exact distribution patterns of body fat are only now becoming known, however. In some racial groups, such as the Hottentot, there seems to be a special disposition for fat to deposit on the buttocks and on the thighs. There are also characteristic differences, on the average, between male and female fat distribution patterns. In American men total body fat appears to increase with age, even in persons who do not gain weight, at least into the fifties. The genetics of fat patterns and the relation of fatness to disease are problems now being actively studied by anthropologists in collaboration with biochemists and physicians.

Facial Growth and Orthodontics.   Many other applications of precise body measurements to the healing arts have called on the skill of anthropometry. One of these, measurement of facial growth in relation to shape of jaws and position of teeth, has called for the combined efforts of anthropologists and orthodontists (dentists specializing in straightening the teeth). Especially among Europeans and peoples of European culture, wherever they live and whatever their race, there is a large proportion whose teeth seem too big for their jaws or whose jaws seem unmatched to each other. While some believe that these disharmonies are inherited, others have demonstrated situations in which dietary and other habits are largely responsible. The teeth may be rotated or crowded out of the tooth row, and upper teeth may fail to meet the lower ones or may do so in an unsatisfactory manner. Such conditions interfere with adequate chewing and are considered ugly. To correct these malformations, orthodontists move the teeth in the jaw by the application of mechanical forces. Unless the orthodontist can predict the amount of future growth of the jaws of children, the process may not be effective or may produce other maladjustments.

To obtain adequately accurate measurements of growth potential, anthropologists and radiologists have devised a number of techniques to X ray the head under standardized conditions that permit the restudy of the same individual later. These are called techniques of *cephalometry*. Experimental methods are also used. Animals are injected with a dye that stains growing bone but not already formed bone. These studies demonstrate that each cranial bone grows more or less independently at its various edges and, in some cases, surfaces. The way to take the measurements for orthodontic purposes, however, can best be determined by the practical test of usefulness in treating patients. In the basic studies of the anthropologist, the best units for the study of growth in man may be suggested by the natural units of growth observed in experimental animals whose bones are stained with a dye.

11

Evolution and the Future

The evolution of man has been a long and complex process, but it is not complete. If man's evolutionary line persists for millions of years into the future, as it well may do, the populations will eventually be so different from today's *Homo sapiens* as to be considered new species. Fortunately, the process of natural selection will insure that any hereditary advantages we may have will tend to be transmitted to those descendants. On the other hand, any of our traits which tend to handicap our offspring will be eliminated by the same process and replaced by other traits of other people. New features or combinations may arise. Despite the tendency to adapt, the extinction of the human species is not altogether impossible.

One threat is the population explosion. It is safe to predict that the human population will continue to increase tremendously in the near future. If they face shortages of food and other goods, men may set in motion conflicts which will destroy all mankind. The threat must be given sober consideration by scientists, clergymen, educators, politicians, and the populace in general. We are reducing the death rate, while the birth rate is far from under control; therefore, disaster from the sheer weight of numbers looms as a future prospect.

Aside from the danger of overpopulation, man is faced with threats to the quality of the human population. Genetic deterioration can occur through increased radiation levels of atmosphere, food, and water. Furthermore, the proportion of genetic defects will increase if those who can have defective children have large families. Such deterioration might outstrip the ability of modern medicine, drugs, clothing, etc., to compensate for weaknesses. Radiation from atomic tests definitely increases the number of mutations in a population, and these mutant genes are, in most cases, harmful. Furthermore, unless society finds ways to encourage more prudent behavior, some parents of offspring with hereditary defects will try to compensate for the defective child by having further children (who may also be defective or capable of transmitting the defect). Many scientists believe that the human gene pool is slowly degenerating. One measure suggested to arrest this trend is the promotion of so-called *eugenics*.

Eugenics is the pursuit of methods designed to improve hereditary qualities. It involves a number of delicate ethical problems: The question of the deliberate choice of mates for a reproduction aimed at superior physical qualities (and this again involves difficult judgments), or the decision whether to reproduce or not, are part of the eugenic concern. Partially because of public reaction to overenthusiastic and sometimes erroneous claims of its adherents, the eugenic movement so far has had little effect in eliminating hereditary diseases or otherwise modifying the average quality of future generations. If the risks of abuses such as those fostered in the name of race hygiene in Nazi Germany can be eliminated by substituting voluntary for forced measures, eugenics may become an important factor in the future. Today the effects of "planned parenthood" in such countries as the United States seem to be to bring the number of offspring of families close to a generally accepted idea of a "normal" family. Couples with many children may wish not to add to their family, but those with no children often wish to increase their chance of having a baby. In the eyes of many people the desire for many children is justified by traditions based on past experience when a large family actually did mean wealth and prestige; but under modern conditions the security of the whole society may be endangered if this attitude prevails, since it may spell the danger of mass starvation.

Likewise, in respect to quality of future generations, society has a stake and public policies have long been influenced by this problem. The sexes are usually kept separate in institutions for mental defectives, for instance. But private concern in the problems is recent and shared by few people.

For the future, regardless of the legal restraints in one or another country, it seems likely that artificial insemination—with the possibility of a single father for scores of children—will be practiced in some places. Moreover, with techniques now under development, semen (the fluid which contains the male sex cells) can be preserved so that men long dead may be able to sire children. This may lead to close inbreeding, which in turn brings other genetic dangers—an increase of homozygous defects and elimination of potentially adaptive variability.

In the future, also, man may be able to affect the likelihood of having male or female offspring: Sperm determining the two sexes differ so that it may become possible to sort out the two kinds.

The various prospects of such application of purpose to what has hitherto largely been left to chance can be estimated in advance and studied in process by human geneticists; we already are able to identify an imminent danger to the species before it is swamped by a load of disadvantageous genes. The trouble is that the gap between scientific and popular knowledge in this respect appears to be widening. And this is the reason why some of our schools are greatly increasing their provision for the study of human evolution, past, present, and potential.

There is no assurance of human "progress." The impact of human activities, which can release toxic substances and radiation into the air we breathe and the food we eat, may outstrip natural or deliberate selection. Natural history, too, imposes new conditions: Changes in the animals, plants, things, and climates that surround us. And man goes on changing his relationship to his environment. The world is rapidly becoming one in which the immediate surroundings and resources are losing the direct influence they have had on human evolution through the selective process man shares with the animal world. Not only is more of the environment man-made, but the local environment becomes almost inconsequential for continued human evolution as man's world becomes more mobile and his larger environment makes new demands on body and mind. This calls for a high degree of plasticity in responding to different natural and artificially produced conditions. Space travel and living on other planets may add yet another dimension to the environment in which man must be able to function in order to survive. At least he must leave his offspring equipped with the essential capacities for effective mastery of the total environment.

This account of human evolution has covered great spans of the past through an analysis of the fossil primates. Emphasis has also been given to the evolution that is going on in man today. But whether through the long-term changes seen in the fossil record or through the short-term changes of population genetics, the key to understanding evolution in the future lies in an analysis of the processes involved. And, as Garrett Hardin, professor of biology at the University of California at Goletta, says in *Nature and Man's Fate:*

> It doesn't much matter whether you think man was created out of dust six thousand years ago or came from apes a million years earlier . . . Believe what you will of evolution in the past: but you had jolly well better believe it will take place in the future if you hope to make political decisions that will give your descendants a reasonable chance to exist.

Furthermore, in such a time as ours, progress along the established lines, however great it has been in the recent past, cannot be held to meet the need for new knowledge. There is needed also a new vigor in approach to both old and new problems. The best evidence that physical anthropology possesses this vigor lies in the uncompromising directness with which so many of its practitioners are attacking complex problems. Without abandoning the rigor of proven methods, or the painful accumulation of detailed additions to knowledge that has been so fruitful in the past, they are willing to re-examine concepts that may no longer suffice to explain the multitude of collected data, and to explore new hypotheses that would account for a wider range of facts. They are creating a theoretical basis of physical anthropology in closer harmony with the now rapidly changing conceptual structure of the universe and of man's place in it.

Biologists, physicians, anatomists, historians, geneticists, and psychologists continue to raise questions about man's origin and to look for a key to their common problems. The processes of human evolution and differentiation require for their understanding not only the development of general principles but also the application of scientific methods and the future development, or borrowing from other disciplines, of specialized skills.

In physical anthropology there are branches where, as has been shown, general theory and methodology are sufficiently far advanced to permit considerable specialization, both in further research and in application to specific problems. The greatest need and the greatest opportunity for the development of the science is to be found, however, in the search for understandings of the origin of man, of the functioning of his body as a whole, of its responses to the environment, and of its evolutionary potential.

Bibliography

Darwin, Charles. *The Voyage of the Beagle.* New York: Bantam, 1958.

Dobzhansky, Theodosius. *Mankind Evolving.* New Haven: Yale University Press, 1962.

Dunn, L.C. *Heredity and Evolution in Human Populations.* Cambridge, Mass.: Harvard University Press, 1959.

Hardin, Garrett. *Nature and Man's Fate.* New York: Holt, Rinehart and Winston, 1959.

Hooton, E.A. *Man's Poor Relations.* New York: Doubleday Doran, 1942.

Howells, W.W. *Mankind in the Making.* New York: Doubleday and Co., 1959.

Korn, Noel, and Harry Reece Smith. *Human Evolution.* New York: Holt, Rinehart and Winston, 1959.

Oakley, K.P. *Man the Tool-Maker.* (second edition) London: British Museum (Natural History), 1950.

The Race Concept. New York: U.N.E.S.C.O., Columbia University Press, 1952.

Washburn, S.L. *Tools and Human Evolution.* San Francisco: Scientific American Offprint, W.H. Freeman and Co., 1960.

Glossary

Adaptive radiation. Evolution of several kinds of animals each in a different environment from a single previous line.

Allele. One of two or more alternative genes that occupy the same location on the chromosome and that therefore may pair with each other in heredity.

Amino acids. The chemical "building blocks" of proteins, hence found in all living things.

Anthropoid. Manlike; applied to animals that most closely resemble man, the apes.

Anthropometry. The measurement of the human body.

Antibodies. Substances in blood plasma that react with certain proteins.

Archeology. The excavation and study of the remains of ancient man and his works.

Australopithecus. A fossil form from South Africa with some manlike and some apelike features and, by extension, other fossil remains of similar forms.

Blood groups. A classification based on substances of the red blood cells; different in different individuals.

Breeding group. The group within which mates are found, hence the group which will share descendants.

Carbon-14 method. A technique for determining the date at which carbon-containing remains were parts of living organisms; done by measuring the proportion of carbon-14 which has persisted.

Cenozoic Era. The period of time from about 71,000,000 years ago until the end of the glacial epoch some 11,000 years ago.

Cephalometry. Measurement of the head, especially by means of X ray.

Chelles-Acheul industry. Types of crude stone tools found at Chelles and St. Acheul in France and at other places.

Chordates. The animal phylum whose members have a notochord; includes man.

Chromosomes. Microscopic bodies within the nuclei of cells; they contain the material responsible for heredity.

111

Convergence. Evolutionary development of similiar adaptations in different forms.

Cultural anthropology. The study of man's learned behavior and customs.

DNA. Deoxyribonucleic acid, a substance found in chromosomes and capable of reproducing itself and of transmitting hereditary information.

Dominant gene. A gene whose effect is evident in a heterozygote.

Embryo. The early stage of development within the womb.

Enzymes. Organic chemicals that serve to speed up certain chemical reactions.

Eugenics. The application of genetics to the biological improvement of man.

Eutheria. Placental mammals.

Evolution. Heredity with change, especially biological changes continuing over many generations.

Fossil. The remains, frequently petrified bone, of a prehistoric organism.

Gene. The part of a chromosome responsible for the transmission and development of a particular effect.

Gene pool. The totality of genes in a population; it is characterized by gene frequencies.

Generalized. Possessing potential for adaptive radiation.

Genetics. The study of heredity.

Genotype. The genetic make-up of an individual.

Genus. A unit of classification of organisms encompassing related species.

Gerontomorphic. Having physical characteristics resembling those of the aged.

Heterozygous. Having different allelic genes in the pair of chromosomes of the same individual.

Homo Sapiens. The species to which all living human beings belong.

Homozygous. Having the same allelic gene at a particular location on both of a pair of chromosomes.

Mammals. Vertebrates that nurse their young.

Mastoid process. A bony prominence of the skull behind the ear lobe; distinctively developed in man.

Metaphase. The stage in mitosis when the chromosomes are paired and aligned.

Mitosis. A process for the orderly and equal distribution of chromosomal material from one cell nucleus to two forming from it.

Monotremes. Egg-laying mammals.

Mousterian. The type of stone tool found with Neandertal Man in Europe.

Mutation. A change within a chromosome that can then be transmitted; they may be spontaneous or induced by X rays and other agents.

Natural selection. The tendency of those individuals that leave most offspring to be genetically better endowed than others in respect to characteristics which make for survival in the same natural setting.

Neandertal Man. Fossil human form that evolved in the last interglacial period and disappeared after the last glaciation, about 50,000 years ago.

Oreopithecus. A fossil Primate that lived in swampy areas in Italy during the Pliocene Epoch.

Ovum. The female egg cell.

Paleontology. The study of fossils.

Parallelism. Similar evolutionary developments going on separately in related forms.

Pebble-tool. The most primitive type of deliberately worked stone implement known, made of water-worn stones with a few chips removed.

Pedomorphic. Referring to adult physical features that resemble those of a child.

Peking Man. Fossils of *Homo erectus* found near Peking, China.

Phenotype. The observable characteristics of an individual without reference to his genetic constitution.

Pithecanthropus erectus. *Homo erectus,* especially the specimens from Java.

Pleistocene Epoch. The period of continental glaciations; it extended from about 1,000,000 years ago to about 11,000 years ago.

Population genetics. The relations between the breeding that takes place within a population and the hereditary differences among the members.

Potassium-argon method. A technique for determining the date at which certain rocks were formed by measuring the subsequent radioactive decay.

Primates. Man, apes, monkeys and prosiminans.

Proconsul. A primitive monkey-like ape of the Miocene Epoch; the name means "before Consul," a gorilla in the London zoo.

Prognathism. Protrusion of the face, especially forward jut of the part holding the front teeth.

Prosimians. "Pre-monkeys," the most ancient suborder of the Primates.

Race. A subgroup of a species.

Random genetic drift. Chance changes in gene frequencies from generation to generation, as contrasted with natural selection in which the changes can be traced to specific factors.

Recessive gene. A gene whose characteristic effect is seen only in the homozygote, that is, with the gene on both of a pair of chromosomes.

Rhodesian Man. Fossil Neandertaloid human remains from Broken Hill, Northern Rhodesia, Africa. The supraorbital torus is huge.

Sex-differentiating chromosomes. The X and Y chromosomes that determine sex.

Solo Man. A somewhat Neandertaloid fossil human form from Java that resembles *Homo erectus* in some respects.

Specialization. The development of an organ or part that tends to adapt those who possess it for life in a particular environment.

Species. A unit of classification of plants or animals that includes those which can interbreed and thus form a single natural breeding population.

Supraorbital torus. The boney prominence above the eye; it is especially marked in some forms of fossil man.

Spermatozoa. Male sperm cells.

Vertebrates. Animals with backbones.

Villafranchian period. The time during which certain now-extinct animal species prevailed; it is usually considered to represent the beginning Pleistocene, but probably started earlier and ended with the early glaciation, about 600,000 years ago.

Viviparous. Giving birth, as contrasted with oviparous, laying eggs.

Index

Adaptive radiation, 63–64
Alleles, 34
America, early man in, 93
Amino acids, 21
Animal kingdom, man in, 43–46;
    classification of man in, 45
Animals, fossils of, 69
Anthropoidea, 51–57
Anthropology, physical, 7–10
Anthropometry, 9, 95
Ape(s), 54–59; chimpanzee, 57;
    gerontomorphic, 65; gibbon, 53,
    54; gorilla, 55–57, 56; oran-
    gutan, 54–55; posture of great,
    74; relationship to man, 57–58
Archeologist, 7
Artificial insemination, 105
Athletes, racial study of, 41
Australopithecus fossils, discovery
    of, 73–78; gait of, 75–78; pos-
    ture of, 74; skulls and jaws of,
    74–75, 76, 77
Axes, hand, 81

Baboons, 53–54
Biological basis, of life, 19–32
Bipedal, 54
Bisexual reproduction, 43
Body fat, of man, 101
Breeding group, 34
Breeding isolates, 34
Breeding population, 33–39
Broom, Dr. Robert, 73

Carbon, 25
Carbon-14 dating, 93
Carnivores, 63
Cave painting, 91
Cebus monkey, 52

Cenozoic era, 69–71; time scale of,
    69
Cephalic index, 95
Cephalometry, 102
Chelles-Acheul industry, 76, 82
Chemical evolution, of organic
    compounds, 21–22
Chimpanzee, 57
Chordates, 44–45
Chromosomes, of female cell, 30–
    31; of fruit fly, 20; and genes,
    19–20; human; 28–29; meta-
    phase of, 28; sex differentiating,
    29–31
Convergence, of humming bird
    and hummingmoth, 62; and par-
    allelism, 61–63
Crick, and Watson, 24–25
Crossbreeding, of peas, 31
Cross-sectional growth study, 98
Culture, a human phenomenon,
    59–60
Cytochemistry, 24

Dart, Professor Raymond, 73
Darwin, Charles, 17
de Buffon, George Louis Leclerc,
    98
Degree of isolation, 34
Degree of prognathism, 95
Differential growth, of man, 100–
    101
Dinosaurs, 63; age of, 69
DNA (deoxyribonucleic acid), 24–
    26; division of, 24; functions in
    heredity, 25; molecule, 24–25;
    nucleotides, 26
Dollo, Louis, 65
Dubois, Eugene, 79

Embryo, 46
Enzymes, 23
Eocene epoch, 69–70
Era, Cenozoic, 69–72
Eugenics, 104
Eutheria, 45
Evolution, 11–17; and the future, 103–107; generalized and specialized forms of, 64; and genetics, 33; missing link in, 15, 79; and natural selection, 33, 36–38; reversible, 65–66; theories and facts of, 15–17, through uneven increase in numbers, 13–15; varying tempo of, 66
Evolutionary processes, and paleontological principles, 61–67
Extinction, of population, 66–67; of human species, 103
Eye color, 29
Eye-ear plane, 96

Facial growth, and orthodontics of man, 101–102
Family size, variability of, 39
Fossil forms, 15, 61
Fossil man, 79–93, 89; Middle Pleistocene, 82
Fossil primates, 69–78
Fossils, animal, 69; Australopithecus, 73–78; Oreopithecus, 72–73

Gene(s), 17; and chromosomes, 19–20; dominant, 31, 34; recessive, 31, 34
Gene frequencies, 34
Gene mutation, 35–36
Gene pool, 34, 40
Generalized forms, 64
Genetic drift, random, 38–39
Genetics, 16; and evolution, 33; human 27–32; population, 33–41
Geological time scale, 69–70
Gerontomorphic features, 65
Gibbon, 53, 54
Goodman, Dr. Morris, 58
Gorilla, 55–57, 56

Growth differential, in man, 100–101
Growth and health, of man, 98–100
Growth study, 99 (chart); cross-sectional, 98; longitudinal, 98

Hand axes, 81
Hardin, Garrett, 106
Health and growth, of man, 98–100
Hereditary characteristics, 12
Heredity, DNA functions in, 25
Heterozygous, 29
Hominoidea, 45
Homo, 45, 59–60
Homo erectus (Pithecanthropus), 79–80, 81–83, 86, 88–89
Homo sapiens, 45, 60, 83, 90, 92, 93, 103
Homozygous, 29
Horseshoe crab, 14
Human culture, 59–60
Human genetics, 27–32; variability of, 27–28
Human physique, variations in, 9
Human race, 39–41
Human species, extinction of, 103; genetic deterioration of, 103
Hummingbird, convergence of hummingmoth and, 62
Hybrids, breeding of, 31
Hydrogen, 24, 25
Hydrogen bomb, genetic effects of, 36

Inheritance, biological, 27
Insectivores, 50–51
Irradiation, ultraviolet, 22
Isolation, of mating, 39

Java Man, skull of, 80

Leakey, Dr. and Mrs. L. S. B., 71–73, 83
Lemur, ring-tailed, 48
Life, biological basis of, 19–32; origin of, 22–23; theory of natural origin of, 22

Living things, capacity to reproduce, 23
Longitudinal growth study, 98
Loris, **49**

Mammals, 45–47; fossils of, 69; placental, 63–64
Man, in America, 93; in the animal kingdom, 43–46; biological evolution of, 9; body fat in, 101; classification of, 45; cultural influences on, 27; differences in generations of, 11–13, **12**; facial growth and orthodontics, 101–102; fossil, 79–93, 89; generalized form of, 64; gerontomorphic features in, 65; growth measurement of, 97–98; Java, **80**; measurement of, 95–102; Neandertal, 83–86; origin of modern, 89–92; pedomorphism in, 65; Peking 80–81; process of change in, 11–15; racial differences of, 8; relationship of living great apes to, 57–58; Rhodesian, **86**, **87**–88; Solo, **85**, 86–88; specialized form in, 64
Marsupials, 46
Mastoid process, 79
Mating, isolation, 39
Measurement, of man, 95–102; growth of man, 97–99
Mendel, Gregor Johann, 17, 31
Mendel's principles, 31–32
Mesozoic period, 63
Metaphase, of cells, **28**
Metazoa, 45
Miocene epoch, 69–70
Missing link, in evolution, 15, 79
Mitosis, of cells, 19, 28
Modern man, origin of, 88–92
Molecule, DNA, 24–25
Monkey(s), 48–53, 59; cebus, **52**; of Central and South America, 51–52; new world, 51–52, 71; old world, 52–54; pre-monkeys (Prosimians), 48–50; spider, **55**
Monotremes, 46
Mousterian, stone tools, 84
Mutants, 36

Mutation, 34, 35–36
Mutation rates, 35; affected by irradiation, 41

Natural selection, 16, 33–34, 36–38
Neandertaloids, 83–86
Neurospora, 23
Nitrogen, 25

Oligocene epoch, 69–70
Orangutan, 54–55
Order primates, 47–60
Oreopithecus fossils, 72–73
Organic compounds, chemical evolution of, 21–22
Origin of modern man, 88
Ova, 30
Oxygen, 25

Paleocene epoch, 69
Paleontological principles, and evolutionary processes, 61–67
Paleontologist, 7
Parallelism, and convergence, 61–63
Peas, crossbreeding of, 17
Pedamorphism, in man, 65
Peking man, 80–81
Phenotype, 34
Phosphorus, 25
Phyla, 44
Physical anthropology, 7–10
Pithecanthropus (Homo erectus), 79–80; skull of, **80**
Planned parenthood, in United States, 104
Plant synthesis, 22
Pleistocene epoch, 69–70
Pliocene epoch, 69–70
Population, breeding, 33–39; changes in, 13–15; differences in, 40–41; increase in, 103
Population genetics, 33–41
Primates, 7, 70–73; behavior of, 58–59; fossil, 69–78; the order, 47–60
Proconsul, 71–72
Prognathism, degree of, 95
Prosimians, 48–50

Protein(s), 22; polio virus, 58; of primates, 58; serum, 58; synthesis of, 22

Race, human, 39–41; biological differences of, 41; superiority of, 40
Radiation, 43; adaptive, 63–64; genetic effects of, 36
Radioactivity, genetic effects of, 35–36
Random genetic drift, 38–39
Random selection, 34
Recessive gene, 31, 34
Reproduction, 23–26; bisexual, 43
Retzius, Dr. Anders, 95
Rhodesian Man, 87–88, skull of, **86**, **87**
RNA, 26

Serum proteins, animal, 58
Sex cells, 30; inheritable mutations in, 36
Sex differences, in humans, 34, 35
Sex-differentiating chromosomes, 29–31
Sex ratio in United States, 34, 35
Sickle-cell disease, 36, 37
Skeletons, 15
Skull, cephalic index, 95; degree of prognathism, 95; mastoid process of, 79; supraorbital torus of, 79, **86**

Solo Man, 86–87, skull of, **85**
Specialized forms, 64
Spermatozoa, 30
Spider monkey, 55
Supraorbital torus, 79, **86**

Table, classification of man in the animal kingdom, 45
Tarsiers, **50**
Time scale of Cenozoic era, 69
Tissue culture, 29
Todd, T. Wingate, 98
Tools, Chelles-Acheul industry, 76, 82; hand axes, **81**; Mousterian types of, 84, 90, 91; stone, 82, 93
Tree shrew, **51**
Twins, identical, 27

Upper Paleolithic period, cave painting from, **91**; men of, 92

Variability, of human genetics, 27–28
Vertebrates, 44
Villafranchian period, 70–71, 77
Viviparous, 46

Wallace, Alfred Russell, 16
Watson, and Crick, 24–25
Wetzel, N. C., 98–100

X rays, genetic effect of, 35–36